"Follow the life of Tabitha, a teenager tion that causes her to discover things God. Wendy Perry tells a compelling story that many young teens need to hear and can easily identify with in their own lives. She provides a Biblical solution for maturing in Christ. Learning aids are provided, allowing individuals and groups to 'dig deeper' into the helpful instruction."

- **Dr. Terry Faulkenbury**, Founding Pastor of West Cabarrus Church in Concord, NC, and Assistant Professor at Liberty University

"Standing alone, the story grips the reader from the start, but combined with the discussion questions, this becomes a valuable resource for discussion with teenage girls about life and God. Mothers and daughters and groups alike could easily use this format to address what it looks like to really know Christ as maturing girls start to grapple with social struggles and emotions. I highly recommend it."

- **Mindy Brindle**, Missionary in South Asia

"The godly life of author, Wendy Perry, is her best endorsement, along with her excellent writing skills! This captivating adventure, The Battle Within, addresses the primary emotional and spiritual needs experienced by nearly every one of our children. Wendy shares her deep practical wisdom and experience in a non-threatening narrative that the reader will not want to put down. Most importantly, the way to truly know God for oneself is clearly presented, and lives will be changed and enriched by way of this exciting book!

- **Kathie Reimer (Morgan)**, Author

THE BATTLE WITHIN

A Character Journey for Teens

WENDY PERRY

UNITED HOUSE

ISBN: 978-1-952840-04-3

UNITED HOUSE Publishing
Waterford, Michigan
info@unitedhousepublishing.com
www.unitedhousepublishing.com

Cover and interior design: Matt Russell, Marketing Image, mrussell@marketing-image.com

Tabitha Illustration: Brenda Waraniak / ETSY:BETHELOVEDESIGNS

Printed in the United States of America
2021—First Edition

SPECIAL SALES
Most UNITED HOUSE books are available at special quantity discounts when purchased in bulk by corporations, organizations, and special-interest groups. For information, please e-mail orders@ unitedhousepublishing.com.

Thank you:

to my Father God, for entrusting me to write down this story,

to my husband, who is my stable man in all the craziness of life,

to my children, for making me a mom and keeping my prayer life active (insert wink here)

and to my mom, who is my biggest cheerleader.

I love you all greatly!

TABLE OF CONTENTS

ONE: CONFUSION 9

TWO: CONTROL 19

THREE: LONELINESS 29

FOUR: FRUSTRATION 37

FIVE: BITTERNESS 45

SIX: ENVY 53

SEVEN: ANGER 61

EIGHT: SHAME 71

NINE: DREAD 79

TEN: ENLIGHTENMENT 89

ELEVEN: HOPE 103

TWELVE: BLESSINGS 113

ACTIVITIES 123

CITATIONS 135

ABOUT THE AUTHOR 137

ONE

CONFUSION

Just a little closer. She began cautiously inching her way to the scene that was so inviting. It was serene but loud. The roar of the gushing water had a calming effect that made her want to sit and rest. It was beautiful but powerful. The river lazily sparkled in the sunshine and exploded with force over the edge. She had to see more; just enough of a view to see the plummet of the cascading waterfall, to drink in the scene below, and to breathe in the sweet smell of earth and water mixed together.

Suddenly, her skin prickled with fear. The warm rays of the sun were blocked, and she felt so cold as the wind started to fiercely blow and pick up debris along its path. She felt a dark presence behind her and quickly spun around. A black cloud moved towards her to consume her, to trap her in its impenetrable darkness. She knew she had to run, to escape the dark presence before it enveloped her-controlled her. She knew it had the ability to blind her from the beauty and peacefulness around, causing her to only see disappointment, ugliness, and sadness. She turned to flee and stepped on a slippery, moss-covered rock. Her foot stumbled, and down she went into the rushing, ice-cold water. She screamed, arms and legs flailing, and plummeted towards the ground. She would not only see where the waterfall ended; she'd feel it as well. The inviting and beautiful waterfall had now turned into an unwelcoming and terrifying place. Right before her body slammed into the half-submerged boulders below, her body jerked awake.

Sitting up quickly, she hit her head on something hard. Lying back down, she winced with pain, realizing she had a bump on the back of her head, adding to the one she'd just made to her forehead. Her head pounded at each beat of her heart. She opened her eyes and was met with the same blackness as when they were closed. She blinked over and over and rubbed her eyes, squinting, to try and make out a shape, a color, anything—but she could only see a black that was darker than anything she could ever have imagined. Fear seized her. Had hitting her head caused problems with her sight?

As the headache intensified, she knew she needed help. She cried out over and over, but each call was met with her echo. In fact, all she could hear besides her echo was her own breathing, which was becoming quicker and louder. The air seemed heavy and nasty. As fear spread through her, she willed herself to calm down.

"Take slow deep breaths. Slower, slower," she said to herself. After she got her breathing under control, she began to realize her whole body ached; not just her head. Wincing, she felt her thighs, stomach, and arms aching. She felt scrapes, bumps, and blood through her torn clothing.

Now confusion was taking the place of fear and pain. What had happened to her? Why was she so bruised and battered? Where was she? Why couldn't she remember anything? Panic started to rise again. "Stop it!" she whimpered. "I can't panic now." In between trying to take deep breaths, she whispered, "Okay; just calm down. I need to remember what I do know." She knew who she was: Tabitha, thirteen years old. She was the daughter of Jerry and Whitney, the middle child of three, wedged between her older sister, Sarah, and her little brother, Jacob. *Middle*. She didn't really know how to describe herself except to use the word, *middle*. That word sparked a lot of memories about herself. She was medium...average; neither tall nor short, thin nor fat, with hair that was neither straight nor curly. She was neither smart nor dumb, not happy, but not too miserable. She was sort of just in the middle of everything. Not excelling, special, or great at anything. Tabitha felt she didn't know who she was most of the time, and it was painful and unfair. Yeah; her parents loved her. Her siblings were annoying and didn't understand personal space or privacy, but they were okay. But besides that, she felt lonely and friendless because she couldn't seem to fit in with anyone at school or church anymore. "Who am I, really? And, where am I? I feel so confused about everything. How could I be so stupid that I don't know where I am or how I got here?" she spat out in frustration.

Then she remembered the dream that woke her up. Oh, how she longed to be at the beautiful waterfall. The river and waterfall had made her feel so calm and free. Tabitha was not battling her emotions there; instead, she'd felt peace. She'd been able to focus on the beauty around her. But when the dark cloud suddenly appeared, it had wanted to take her away from the tranquility to an ugly, sad place. In real life, that place was actually not a location. It was more about her mindset. Like a black cloud covering the light, her negative thoughts would blind her from seeing the beauty, the positives in her life. Tabitha knew she had many blessings, but it seemed she couldn't control those negative thoughts and emotions that clouded the view of the good things. She longed for a way to escape the negativity, just like she remembered trying to flee the dark presence in her dream.

While she was still thinking about the dream, the cold started to hit her; the kind of cold that seeped through her clothes and her skin all the way to her bones. She slowly started to move her hands around where she lay, trying to feel what she was lying on and to figure out where she was. It soon registered that the cold she felt was coming from rock and a small puddle of water. Raising her hands over her head, she felt more rock above her. Being careful not to hit her head again on the unseen rock, she used her hands to maneuver her body to a sitting position, crying out in pain, when she moved her knees. Tenderly touching them, she knew her knees and hands were in bad shape, as though she had been crawling on the rock for hours. Had she? Why? Shaking her head, she willed it to bring back any memory that could explain her situation. All she saw was darkness, and all she felt was heaviness.

After sitting for a few minutes, in a failed attempt to understand what had happened, she knew she had to figure out her situation without her sight. She had to fight the desire to close her eyes and rest. She had to get up and find her way home.

Instead of crawling on her knees, she decided to scoot on her bottom, first letting her hands feel the surrounding area. It was a slow process, but after a few minutes, she realized she was in a hole about the width and length of her twin bed. She must be in some sort of cave.

Knowing she had to have entered from some point, she decided to be brave. In the area where her outstretched hands could not feel the rock ceiling, she decided to slowly stand up. Halfway to standing, she met the slanted ceiling with her hands and began moving them in all directions. To her joy, she found what felt like an opening, which must have been the place where she entered the small cave. There was still only darkness, but she knew she needed to escape this space, as it felt like it was shrinking around her.

She picked up her foot to begin hoisting herself up, but her foot quickly slid right off the stone. At that moment, she remembered her bucket list: rock wall climbing had always been near the top, but this was not how she wanted to mark it off her list. At least it would be an interesting story to record in her journal.

She just wanted to complete the task so she could be up and out of this place. She wanted to see again. She wanted to remember how she ended up here. She wanted to see her family again. She wanted to be warm and safe. "Stop whining and do this already," she whispered harshly to herself. Feeling around the rock for a non slippery path, she started her ascent: climb a little, slip a little, climb a little more, slip a little more. Tears of frustration flowed, and the pain continued to pound in her head, until she finally reached the top. She knew the wall was only about six feet in height, but the slippery surface and pain in her body made it feel like she was climbing a slip 'n slide on the side of a mountain.

DIGGING DEEPER

You have now started a journey with dear Tabitha.

Throughout the following pages, you will read many things she will experience and discover about herself and God. As you take this journey with Tabitha, I hope you will learn with her along the way.

To help you work through each situation she experiences, questions will follow different stages in Tabitha's journey. Please take the time to think through each question, and answer with complete honesty. Your study and answers will aid you in learning more about yourself just like Tabitha will be doing.

The Battle Within: *Confused*

Merriam-Webster defines *confused* as "disoriented with regard to one's sense of time, place or identity."

This state of being seems to fit Tabitha well at the moment. She awakens from a dream that was, at first, inviting, but quickly turned frightening. Then, she realized she didn't know where she was or how she got there. Lastly, she seemed to be confused about who she was and how she fit in with others.

1. What are your thoughts about Tabitha's dream? Can you relate?

2. What would your reaction have been to finding yourself alone, in a dark place, and unable to see?

3. What are your first thoughts about how Tabitha describes herself?

4. Write a description of yourself–your appearance, your talents/skills, hobbies, etc.

*Now, read Psalm 139:13-18. Compare these verses to what you wrote about yourself above.

"For you formed my inward parts;
you knitted me together in my mother's womb.
I praise you, for I am fearfully and wonderfully made.
Wonderful are your works;
my soul knows it very well.
My frame was not hidden from you,
when I was being made in secret,
intricately woven in the depths of the earth.
Your eyes saw my unformed substance;
in your book were written, every one of them,
the days that were formed for me,
when as yet there was none of them.
How precious to me are your thoughts, O God!
How vast is the sum of them!
If I would count them, they are more than the sand.
I awake, and I am still with you."

5. Similar to Tabitha, do you have a bucket list of activities you would like to accomplish? If not, consider writing one. Write down a variety of activities that you could do now and some that are big dreams for the future. Consider showing your list to your parents and friends. Maybe you could start by doing some of those activities with them and mark them off your list! Don't forget to keep a journal of your experiences.

YOUR NOTES

CONFUSION

TWO

CONTROL

Finally making it to the top of what felt like a slippery mountain, Tabitha gingerly rolled over and rested her back against the cold, rough wall to try and calm herself again. Why did this have to happen? Why was she such a wimp? In the eerily quiet darkness, she had so many questions racing through her head. The rush of emotions she was feeling made it difficult to concentrate. She tried to focus on what she knew, which was that she had to keep moving forward. The movement would at least help her feel that she was making some kind of progress in this dark, unknown space. With the determination to be brave and overcome her weakness, she got up.

She felt the wall and ceiling around her and slid her foot carefully to begin, but then bumped into something soft. She kicked it a couple of times to make sure it wasn't an animal. Since it did not move, she knelt to feel what the object could be. Her hands brushed a bulky object that was covered in a slightly coarse fabric; it had pouches and zippers. Instantly, she recognized what it was. It was her backpack!

A memory popped in her head. *She was in the woods, tears streaming down her face, backpack on her back. Her cellphone was in her left hand, and she was running, using her right hand to guard her face from the branches that seemed to reach out and slap her. She couldn't remember why she was running, but she could feel the urgency to escape something.*

After the memory flashed, all she could do was hug her backpack. She must have run in this dark tunnel, tripped, dropped her backpack in the process, and then fallen into the cave below. She probably hit her head and blacked out for a few minutes. At the moment, it did not matter. She had her backpack, and it held many of her precious treasures. Even without seeing it, she knew what it looked like: dark blue with a starry night scene and many zipper pockets, which held all her precious cargo inside. It was complete with a homemade paracord keychain, her favorite superhero charm at the end. Her mother loved to joke with her, saying that the backpack was her 'magic bag.' She was always pulling things out of the bag like it had a never-ending bottom. Tabitha actually took pride in her backpack. She liked to be prepared. She enjoyed feeling like she had some kind of control; that she would be prepared for any unexpected event that might happen in her life, which seemed to be filled with the unexpected. She opened each compartment of her backpack and took inventory of all her treasured possessions.

Starting from the outside, she felt in the right pocket for her favorite blue water bottle. It was there, still snapped in place. On the opposite side of the bag was a zipper pocket containing a tin of mints. These were the easiest items to get to; she placed them there for a good reason. Tabitha never knew when she might get an annoying tickle in her throat during class, which, if not caught in time, would turn into an ugly coughing spell, complete with eyes watering, nose dripping, and ultimately, her dancing around while gagging, trying hard not to throw up. This little tickle throat dance, if not subdued quickly, would become the most liked video on Facebook because *someone* in class had been videoing it all. She had been there and done that. Shelby. That was the wicked "someone" who'd done it to her. She'd always seemed to be there at Tabitha's most humiliating moments. From then on, water and mints were a *must* in her backpack.

Too, she always had a bag of cashews, right beside the tin of mints, for that much-needed protein, in case she forgot to eat while rushing to catch the bus. A packet of baby wipes was in the front pocket of the backpack, in the event she was to stumble in a puddle while running to catch the bus and need to wipe off mud from her pants. Yes, that had happened to her before as well. Thankfully, no one had a cellphone on the ready for that muddy moment, but it still hadn't stopped Shelby from tweeting about the "klutz clucking like a hen in the mud."

The zipper pouch behind the wipes held Tabitha's special bag of dark chocolate M&M's. This treat gave her the chocolate fix she needed to brighten her day when everyone and everything around her just kept her in a state of misery. Tissues were located beside the M&M's for when the chocolate didn't work, and the tears leaked out at unexpected moments. A band-aid kit was in the pouch behind the chocolate and tissues, in case she tripped over something and scraped her knee while rushing away to keep Shelby from catching her crying.

She opened the big part of the backpack. She could feel a long, slender pouch that held her pencils and pens. Standing straight up next to the pouch was her journal, which held her secrets and stories of all the horrible things that

CONTROL

happened during the day.

The back compartment, made for a laptop she didn't own, was reserved for her best friends: Books. A book was the most useful item of all. It could not only get her mind off her problems, but it could also become a shield to make her invisible. While everyone else was in a circle of friends laughing and making fun of others, she could bury her nose in her book. It could make her feel not so left out, not so lonely. If anyone dared to approach her, she only had to raise the book higher to hide her eyes, giving the person the nonverbal cue that she was unavailable.

Yeah; maybe some of those girls who approached her seemed nice. They would come up and compliment her, want to share their snack, ask about class, etc. But she was too scared to talk to them. What if they thought she was lame or uninteresting? No; a book was the perfect best friend. It would not want or expect anything from her. She couldn't disappoint the book.

Tabitha knew she was easily misunderstood by her peers and even adults. Many thought she was rude because her face was always set in a serious expression, and she didn't converse easily with others. Because of her quiet ways, she didn't know how to make small talk, and she most definitely did not know how to share her feelings with others, nor did she want to learn. She only allowed the pages of her journal to be filled with her true feelings. The thought of opening herself up like that to others made her feel sick, exposed, and vulnerable. If everyone would just limit talk to books, she'd be able to carry on a great conversation.

Reading was her love and passion. She could talk all day long about how a character felt or the reasons characters did this or that. But as soon as the conversation turned to her own feelings, she would want to hide like a hermit crab sticking its head and claws back in its shell. What if she shared how she really felt and everyone laughed? Or what if they looked at her like she had the day's cafeteria lunch special between her teeth? No, thank you! She did not need that kind of rejection. She even hated the questions her teachers would ask in class or in an essay prompt. Questions like, "What would you feel if you were the main character? Describe your feelings over this injustice." What did it matter? Why did they care? Did the teachers need to have something to laugh about later? "Ha! Look what Tabitha said she felt!"

No; books were her only good friends. They were safe. Too, books were what she had in common with Catherine, the only best friend she had ever had. She had known her for several years from church. Both were shy. Neither one knew how to reach out to the other until they were thrown together for a project. They had to pick a book to read to the five-year-old Sunday School class and create a craft. At their first meeting to plan the project, they immediately bonded over their love of books. In fact, they talked so much about the books they loved, they forgot to choose one for the project! After that initial meeting, they became the best of friends. They seemed strange to others because instead of playing games or watching movies, they would sit on the floor in Tabitha's bedroom and read together. Tabitha had such good memories of the two of them reading *The Wizard of Oz* together. Tabitha was even able to share some of her true feelings with Catherine. Besides her family, she had never felt that comfortable with another person. Then, last year, Catherine had had to move, and her only true companion was gone. For a few months, they tried to video call and read books together, but soon the distance and busyness of life cut those friendship ties.

Oh, how she longed for a true friend though...one to actually be real with. But how could she find one? Now that she was older, how was she supposed to act with a friend? Her family members were the only ones who truly knew her – the good, bad, and ugly. And lately it seemed the bad and ugly were all she knew how to be. Her fits of anger seemed to be breaking out more often. She didn't want to act this way, but it seemed she couldn't help herself. She would say things she didn't mean, scream, and even throw things in anger. It still scared her to think about a time, not long ago, when she'd lost control. Her sister, Sarah, had been invited to an event Tabitha really wanted to attend, but she was never asked. She was feeling down about this, when her parents told her she had to babysit her brother while her sister went out. She felt it was completely unfair and argued with them. She didn't understand why no one had bothered to invite her. She felt like no one cared about her, and the last thing she wanted to do was babysit her little brother. As her parents started lecturing her, she'd felt this intense rage build up and just burst out of her. She began to scream, "Why? Why do I have to watch that brat?" Stomping her feet, she continued, "Why do I have to be punished while Sarah has all the fun?!" Working herself up even more, and without realizing it, she'd started pulling at her hair as she shrilled, "I hate my life!" Not until the pain registered, did she understand what she was doing. The shock of her reaction not only scared her parents but herself too. Why had she let her emotions take over like that? The sadness she felt just seemed to spill over in anger toward any family member around. She would never do that in front of others!

Most people–teachers, church family, neighbors–knew her as a serious, quiet, yet kind teenager. They would be shocked to hear her yelling in anger or to really know her thoughts at those moments. She would only show her real self to her family, and that was just because she lived with them, and there was no way to hide her emotions that long. They would have to go through the pain of knowing her. If she was really going to be honest, she knew they had to love her. She could show her real feelings, knowing they would always love her because they had to–they were family. Plus, they had shown time and again that, despite her fits, they would never give up on her. Others weren't required to love her, so instead of opening herself up to others, only to be rejected, it was just easier to be quiet and never get close to them.

Snapping herself back to the present, she mentally checked off the items she had found in her backpack.

DIGGING DEEPER

The Battle Within: *Control*

Merriam-Webster defines *control* as "to exercise restraining or directing influence over" or "to have power over."

Tabitha loves her backpack and the items it holds. Many times, when people feel they have no control over their surroundings or a situation, they will try to control something tangible. It can bring comfort. Tabitha uses her backpack to comfort herself, to give her a feeling of control or readiness if a situation arises unexpectedly. If she is prepared for the unexpected, she will be able to control it with the items she carries in her backpack.

1. Like Tabitha, do you have something special that helps you feel more in control throughout the day?

2. Can you share your feelings easily? If so, with whom?

3. If you can't share your feelings easily, do you feel you bottle up your emotions until they seem to explode without warning?

It is unhealthy to bottle up emotions and unfair to others receiving the impact of the 'explosion.' It is important to find healthy ways to work through your problems. If talking to your parents or a trusted adult is difficult right now, think about writing down your feelings. Then consider sharing your writing with a trusted adult. But most importantly, God is always present to listen and help.

Many of the Psalms in the Bible are written by David. He poured out his heart– praises and complaints–to God. Learn from him, and remember God is always there to listen to you.

"Trust in him at all times, O people; pour out your heart before him; God is a refuge for us." (Psalm 62:8, ESV)

Spend some time reading a few of David's Psalms. Write down what you learn from the readings. Psalm 6, 8, 16, and 27 are just a few examples of David pouring his heart out to God.

4. Is someone in your life being cruel to you-bullying you? Have you shared this issue with anyone? Bullying is wrong, hurtful, and can cause serious problems. Getting help is not a sign of weakness; it is brave.

YOUR NOTES

CONTROL

THREE

LONELINESS

Now to look for the flashlight. It should be placed right beside the book in the backpack. This item was important for those semi-dark rides home on the bus. The bus was the worst. There were no teachers walking around keeping an eye on everyone. On the bus, the driver was focused on keeping the huge yellow monster between the correct lines and pretending not to see or hear the rowdy kids behind her. If Tabitha were lucky enough to get out of school the fastest, she could manage to sit close to the front to avoid most of the mean kids. Those kids loved to annoy any person who was quiet or the odd one out. Once, she remembered a time when a guy took her backpack and started looking through it. He enjoyed pulling out her stuff and making jokes to his friends about them. From then on, she held her backpack on her lap and tried to avoid eye contact with him or any of his minions. But even when she successfully kept her distance, loneliness could start creeping in; especially in the winter when the darkness started to invade before she was dropped safely at home. So, she used the flashlight to read and escape a feeling that was magnified when she heard the others talking and laughing. Now, where was that flashlight? Maybe, just maybe, her eyesight was not damaged, and it was just dark in the cave. The flashlight would determine that and hopefully, illuminate the way out.

Searching for the flashlight, her fingers instead touched the last thing in her bag- her Bible. It was a pink Bible which read: "God's Girl." It was cute and all, but it was mainly there because her mother said if she was going to have all the other supplies, she needed the Bible. It was supposed to be the most important item of all her supplies; it was her "lifeline to God," or something like that.

Since she was born, her parents took her to church–her "other family," as her parents would say. At five years old, she became a "Cubbie" in the AWANA Bible club. Every Wednesday night, she would put on her AWANA vest with pride. She loved the club when she was younger. It was a weekly program where she would play special games with her friends, learn a truth from the

Bible, and then recite a Bible verse she had practiced all week. Each year, she would move up in the program with excitement. She had been learning Bible verses ever since the first day of the Bible club; it had been fun for the most part, but now she was a teenager.

Now it seemed the rules had changed somehow with the friends at church and school. She just didn't know how to fit in. She couldn't keep up with the new trends and activities. The feeling of being on the outside of the circle looking in was constant now. She felt alone and friendless. Yes, she could blend in with a group. There was always a need for at least one person to stand and just listen. This was how she had gotten by at church. She would stand there silently, letting others talk, and she would always be ready to laugh or sigh in the correct way when the others did. This had always come easy for her, mainly because she depended on her older sister. Sarah was great in a group. She knew how to talk to everyone and make them laugh. When Sarah was around, she felt more at ease because she could rely on her to lead the conversations. Every now and then, though, someone would attempt to include her. Several times, in fact, her small group leader would encourage her to talk with the other girls. She would pull her into the circle with the group and try to include her in their conversations. The leader would ask Tabitha to share something special about herself or tell about a book she recently read. At times, the other girls really seemed interested and would start asking their own questions. That would be the time Tabitha began to feel awkward. When all eyes were focused on her, she would start wondering if they thought she was stupid or childish. Then, with doubts dancing in her head, she would make an excuse to leave quickly, like she needed to meet someone or go to the bathroom…any excuse to flee the attention, questions, and her own fears.

Life held so many problems.

School was harder. Her classmates were meaner. The slightest mistake, and you became the joke of the day. Because of this, she worked hard to look her best, be quiet, and stay out of the way. And then there were her social media accounts. Most days she hated them; they made her feel even lonelier. Though without them, she felt she would be missing out on something important. It was a constant chore to keep up with them, and, in addition, deal with her parents and their never-ending pep talks, lectures, and desire to spend family time together. All the activities that were important in her life had kept her really busy.

With all those problems, reading the Bible, much less memorizing the verses, had become more difficult to do. She was getting by in AWANA to please her parents. They didn't know she memorized the verses the day of, but she got it done, and that was all that mattered. As for her Bible; if it made her mother happy that she carried it in her backpack, she would do it.

Just then, Tabitha realized she was hugging her Bible close to her chest. She laughed at herself. Perhaps, she thought; if it were truly a lifeline, her mother might magically appear. If nothing else, maybe it would get her out of this dark, scary place.

"Guess not," she spat out in anger. "Where are you, all powerful God?" As soon as she said those words, with too much sassiness, as her mother would say, words from a memory verse popped in her mind: "Let the words of my mouth and the meditation of my heart be acceptable in your sight, O LORD, my rock and my redeemer" (Psalm 19:14, ESV).

Hmmm…Guess some of the verses had stuck. But how were they going to help her here?

Returning to her search in her backpack, she still couldn't find the flashlight. Balling her hand into a fist, she let out an exasperated breath and fussed at herself, "So much for being prepared! I always have it. Why not now? Come to think of it; since I'm always so prepared all the time, why am I here in the first place? I would never have gone on an adventure without a plan in place. Honestly; I would never have gone on this type of an adventure, unless my parents had forced me to 'get out of my bubble, and enjoy God's creation.' So, what am I doing here?"

Wanting so badly to answer her questions, Tabitha decided to concentrate on the memory that had flashed back earlier of her running in the woods. Picturing herself in that moment sent a shiver down her body, as the overwhelming feelings of fear, shame and embarrassment washed over her. She had not been on a fun adventure. She had been running from something.

At some point in her race, she had tripped, landing part way under a shrub, as her cell phone flew out of her sweaty left hand. She'd heard it land with a clang and THUD. Knowing that her cellphone was of vital importance, her eyes darted back and forth to try to spot it. It should have stood out against the dingy ground, with its bright yellow case and pop socket. She had begged her parents for the new accessories. Instead of giving her the money like other parents do, they, of course, had had to "teach her the value of working" to pay for the case and pop socket herself because "she would appreciate them more" that way. Now, she just hoped the phone was still working and not broken or shattered. Crawling around the area where she had fallen, she pawed the ground in search of her phone. After a few minutes, her eyes noticed an opening in a rock. She now knew where her phone must have landed.

She reached into her backpack to get her flashlight. With her backpack slung over one shoulder and with a deep breath, she half crawled, half walked to the cave, ready to find her cellphone and escape for a few minutes from the feeling of humiliation that was trying to pull her into a dark despair. Without warning, an old hymn her grandmother had always sung sprang to her mind: "Rock of Ages cleft for me; let me hide myself in Thee." Shocked at the timing of this song, she whispered to herself, "Now where did that come from? Was that a hint? A heavenly push? Whatever it was, I'm going for it."

Entering the hole, she realized the rock floor had a steep decline, which must lead to a cave and probably to where her phone had landed. As she shone her flashlight into the dark hole, she heard a crunch and rustle somewhere close by. Without thinking, she started moving quickly down into the dark cave. She underestimated the angle of the decline and the loose pebbles that rolled under her feet because she soon found herself airborne, arms flailing wildly. She hit the stone and rolled farther down into the abyss. Somewhere during the fall, she must have dropped the flashlight.

DIGGING DEEPER

The Battle Within: *Loneliness*

Merriam-Webster defines *loneliness* as "being without company/cut off from others."

Even amid a group of people, activities, or many friends/followers, you can feel lonely, just like Tabitha. Most people struggle with loneliness at different times in their lives. Feeling lonely can be a result of others excluding you or from you excluding yourself from others.

1. Do you struggle with feelings of loneliness at times? Can you pinpoint the cause of the loneliness?

2. Why would a Bible be considered a "lifeline?" Why would Tabitha's mother want her to carry one?

3. Why did the Bible have "God's Girl" on it? What could that mean, considering the Bible verse, 1 John 3:1a (ESV)?: "See what kind of love the Father has given to us, that we should be called children of God; and so we are."

4. Are you active in church? If so, what is important about church? How can it help you? How can it be "another family?" Read Hebrews 10:24-25 (ESV) to help you answer these questions: "And let us consider how to stir up one another to love and good works, not neglecting to meet together, as is the habit of some, but encouraging one another, and all the more as you see the Day drawing near."

If you aren't attending church, would you consider visiting one?

5. Have you, or do you memorize Bible verses? If so, have you ever had them pop into your mind unexpectedly? Have they guided, convicted, or helped you? Psalm 119:11 and 2 Timothy 3:16-17, give great reasons why it is important to memorize Bible verses:

*Psalm 119:11 (ESV): *"I have stored up your word in my heart, that I might not sin against you."*

*2 Timothy 3:16-17 (ESV): *"All Scripture is breathed out by God and profitable for teaching, for reproof, for correction, and for training in righteousness, that the man of God may be complete, equipped for every good work."*

YOUR NOTES

FOUR

FRUSTRATION

"Stupid, stupid, stupid!" Tabitha yelled. During the hunt to find her flashlight and cell phone, she must have gotten disoriented in the dark and fallen in the small cave below. "I *am* a klutz, just like Shelby says. I fell not only once, but twice, and got myself lost in this stinky, wet cave. Who does this? No wonder no one wants to be my friend. I don't even like myself. I'm stupid with no skills, talents or common sense, and only my family loves me!" In her anger, the words, "God so loved the world, that He gave His only Son," from John 3:16 jolted her. "Stop it! Stop it! If You love me, why am I here? If You love me, why can't anything in my life go right?" Tabitha screamed and hurled the words at a God she thought she believed in when life was simpler, when she smiled and laughed so easily with her family, church family, and her friend. But that was before she had entered junior high, started growing up, and things began changing with her body, her mind, and her peers.

"*If* You are real. *If* You loved me. *If* I was really Your daughter, then You wouldn't let me get hurt or feel so sad and lonely. Life is not supposed to be this way! It isn't like this for Shelby and the other mean kids at school. They have everything! They are the reason why I am unhappy! They are making my life horrible! So, why me? Why does my life stink so much? Did You create me so You could have some enjoyment...someone You could laugh at?" The last words came out as sobs. She knew these thoughts and feelings well. She had experienced them many times. She would stand in front of her bedroom mirror and have these same conversations. Sometimes she would even coerce herself to cry just because it felt good to release her sadness that way. No coercing now; these tears flowed freely.

All her frustration leaked from her eyes, and so many hurtful memories played in her mind. She thought of her school life. She was rarely invited to parties, never picked first for group projects, and she would sit in a corner of the cafeteria because she was too afraid to approach anyone. And almost every teacher she had would say, "Oh you are Sarah's sister. She is a wonderful girl!" Sobbing louder, Tabitha choked out, "I am not my sister! I am my own person. I am capable of being wonderful too." Even at church, Sarah was praised for her outgoing personality. She was known by so many people because she loved to interact with others. Even her brother would receive lots of attention and laughs for his fun-loving nature. He was always being goofy or telling lame jokes. Whimpering she said, "Why don't others notice me?"

When the sobbing started to wind down, she felt something jump on her leg and pitter patter its way across her thigh. With a shudder and shriek, she jumped up, backpack in hand, and moved quickly, not knowing or seeing where she was going. It would be her luck to die in the cave from some rare animal bite. She imagined the newspaper headline would read, "Young Girl Dies Alone in a Dark Cave, Holding Tightly to Her Only Friend: Her Backpack."

Feeling her way with her hands, and picking her feet up high so as not to trip again, she continued to wander. After what seemed like an hour, the stone wall abruptly ended. Where was she now?

Something felt different. A cool breeze swept by her face, but she also felt something like an openness in the dark. She froze. All she could think about was every adventure movie she'd ever watched. She imagined that if she took one wrong step, she would either drop into the mouth of a hungry alligator, be hugged tightly by an eager python, take a melting bath in a lake of lava, or something much, much worse. Her mind changed gears, and she couldn't stop thinking of every scary scene she had seen in all the horror movies she'd watched in secret.

It had not taken long for her parents to find out. Tabitha's overactive mind and reactions made it very obvious. She would jump at the slightest noise, double and triple check the locks at night, and sleep with her lights on, which she had not done since she was five years old. The incident that made it completely clear to her parents was when she'd almost knocked her brother out. He loved to play jokes on the family. One night after dinner, he'd hidden under Tabitha's bed. When he jumped out and screamed, "Boo!" Tabitha went ballistic. Without thinking, she started screaming, swung her arms in defense, hitting her brother in the process, and fled the room to her parents. Once her shaking body had calmed down and her brother had stopped crying from the pain, she had been lectured and grounded. Now she could hear her mother's words repeating Psalm 119:37: "Turn my eyes from looking at worthless things; and give me life in your ways." Frustration took over her fear, when she thought about how her parents always seemed to be right. Not wanting to dwell on another thing she had done wrong lately, she concentrated on her next plan of action.

    "Okay, I don't want my life to end in any of those scenarios. That would be just another thing Shelby could laugh about. So, what do I do?" she asked herself. There was no turning back, since all that lay behind her was a dead end. She hadn't died on her way in, so there had to be a safe way out. The best thing she could do right now was get on her hands and knees. Then as she crawled, she could feel with her hands first, if the ground dropped away. At least she would have time to save herself from falling headlong into a creature's mouth. Nope, she did not want to be lunch for any animal!

    Tabitha dreaded the pain she was going to endure by abusing her already battered hands and knees. First things first; she was going to get her handy dandy band-aid kit and patch up her bleeding scraped hands and knees. Maybe the little bit of padding would help her.

DIGGING DEEPER

The Battle Within: *Frustration*

Merriam-Webster defines *frustration* as "feeling discouragement, anger, and annoyance because of unresolved problems or unfulfilled goals, desires, or needs."

Tabitha is feeling frustration at this point in her journey. She is frustrated with her current situation, herself, others, and God. The feeling of frustration can cause you to behave negatively, want to give up, or it can help you find a determination to fight through and solve the problem.

1. Do you notice all the negative things Tabitha says about herself? Is that helpful for her? Why?

Read Ephesians 4:29 (ESV): *"Let no corrupting talk come out of your mouths, but only such as is good for building up, as fits the occasion, that it may give grace to those who hear."*

2. Tabitha is experiencing a difficult time and blaming everyone, even God. Do you feel that He has forgotten her or doesn't care? Have you ever felt angry with God?

FRUSTRATION

**Read Jesus' parable about the Lost Sheep in Matthew 18:10-14 (ESV):
"See that you do not despise one of these little ones. For I tell you that in heaven their angels always see the face of my Father who is in heaven. What do you think? If a man has a hundred sheep, and one of them has gone astray, does he not leave the ninety-nine on the mountains and go in search of the one that went astray? And if he finds it, truly, I say to you, he rejoices over it more than over the ninety-nine that never went astray. So it is not the will of my Father who is in heaven that one of these little ones should perish."

*What do you think this could mean in Tabitha's situation?

3. Did Jesus ever promise His followers would have an easy life?

**Read John 16:33 (ESV): *"I have said these things to you, that in Me you may have peace. In the world you will have tribulation. But take heart; I have overcome the world."*

4. Why do you think Tabitha was grounded for watching horror movies? Do you think her parents were correct? Right now, all those scary images are popping up in her mind. Do those images help her at all? Explain how Psalm 119:37 can be applied to this situation.

**Psalm 119:37, *"Turn my eyes from looking at worthless things; and give me life in your ways."*

5. How has Tabitha shown determination through her frustrated feelings?

YOUR NOTES

FIVE

BITTERNESS

After bandaging her hands and knees, she felt her shoestrings to make sure they were tied and wouldn't cause her any problems. Feeling her favorite shoes brought back another memory from two months ago that she wished she could forget.

She had received cool, white-with-blue-stripe high-top Vans for her birthday. In her opinion, it was the best birthday present in all her thirteen years. She wore them everywhere, with every outfit-even her church dress, much to her mother's protest. She would have slept in them had she been able. These shoes made her feel cool. She even got a compliment from Stetson, the cutest guy in school. Then, one day, Shelby did her meanest thing yet.

It was lunch time, and Tabitha was sitting outside on the concrete steps, reading her book. Every now and then, she would glance down at her shoes to see how cute they looked. Shelby, acting out of character, glided over, and sat beside her. She set her cup of grape juice down at her feet and started questioning Tabitha about her book. Shelby appeared very interested and excited about what Tabitha was reading. Tabitha was never one to make small talk or answer questions out of the blue. She looked up and stared in surprise and confusion. Before she could figure out how to form an answer to her questions, Shelby winked at her group of friends sitting a few yards away. Then, she stood up and quickly turned her foot so her heel knocked the cup of grape juice over.

As the juice spilled on top of Tabitha's beautiful white Vans, Shelby dramatically placed her hands on her mouth as if to appear surprised and sorry. All the while, she laughed, and her friends took pictures of the 'accident.' The picture that was commented on the most was one of Tabitha with her mouth slightly ajar and a tear rolling down her cheek, just staring down at her purple-stained Vans.

All the teachers believed it was a complete accident, so nothing was done to 'sweet' Shelby. No one asked Shelby and her friends to take down the

45

embarrassing pic because the caption read, "So sorry Tabitha, that I spilled my juice on your cool shoes." No real apology was given to Tabitha face-to-face. No offer to replace her ruined shoes either; only a smirk and a humiliating post.

Tabitha left school early that day because she knew she couldn't hold in her emotions any longer. As soon as she got in her mother's van and slammed the door behind her, every pent-up feeling burst out. As she explained what had happened the volume of her voice continually rose until she was shouting. With her fists beating her backpack, she shouted, "I hate Shelby! I hate all her stupid friends! Everyone thinks she is wonderful; even the teachers! No one knows the truth! No one cares how I feel!" Pulling into a parking space, Tabitha's mother let her just scream it out. Then, she gently took her daughter's fists in her hands. Thankfully, Tabitha's mom believed her. She knew Shelby had done a horrible thing to her, but, of course, she went into one of her teaching moments. Her mother told her all the annoying clichés that she had heard a thousand times... Tabitha needed to take the "high road," "Forgiveness was the key," and "hurt people hurt people," etc. The one that really sent her over the edge was when her mom said, "Shelby must be really hurting and insecure inside."

"What!?" Tabitha spit out with such venom. "Really? Shelby is hurting inside? How can you tell? By all her friends following her around like she is a queen or by how the teachers give her praise for her schoolwork? Is that how you can tell she is hurting inside? Really, Mom, I can't believe you are taking her side! I hate her, and wish I never had to see her again!"

Whatever her mom had said after that, she shut out. She turned her face to the window and seethed in anger. Her mother was now frustrated with her as well, and decided they'd drive home in silence.

When they pulled into their driveway, her mom told her to follow her. It was a command, and Tabitha knew she'd better obey. As they walked to the back of the house, her mom said she'd have to try to let go of this incident with Shelby before bitterness took root and took over.

In the backyard, her mom pointed out the ivy she had planted years ago. Putting her hand lovingly on Tabitha's shoulder, she said, "Originally, I planted this ivy at the bottom of the tree. I thought the green would be a nice splash of color; especially in the winter. Before I knew it, the ivy grew so quickly, I couldn't keep up with it. Now look at what's happened." Tabitha looked and noticed the ivy covered the whole tree, engulfing it from bottom to top. Her mother continued the lesson. "Now, not only is the ivy out of control, but it is weighing the tree down. Soon, I will have to begin the process of pulling out all the ivy in hopes of saving the tree." Her mom paused and looked into Tabitha's eyes with overwhelming tenderness and love. "Tabby, I know Shelby did some-

thing horrible. Right now, you have a choice. You can forgive, even though she never said sorry, and move on, or you can dwell on this and become bitter. But remember this tree. Do you really want to be weighed down with bitterness towards Shelby? The extra weight will only cause you hurt and eventually engulf you in unhappiness."

At that point, Tabitha just felt exhausted. She was still angry but tired of talking about it. She didn't want to think about what her mother had said or to try to forgive Shelby. She wanted to be angry. To try and appease her mom and stop the "advice," she told her mom thanks and that she just needed time alone. Then, she went to her room and imagined all the ways she could get back at Shelby.

She knew her mother was trying to help, but Tabitha did not take her advice. Tabitha's bitter feelings had taken root. Instead of moving on and forgiving, she had thought a lot about what Shelby had done to her. Every time she brought up that horrible memory in her mind, it was as if another vine of bitterness would grow. She felt covered now. And she didn't know how to cut or dig out of the bitterness without causing herself discomfort. She just didn't want to forgive Shelby; it would be too much work for her.

Tabitha tried to push away the memories of her mom's talks and of the ruining of her shoes. She had done her best to bleach her shoes, but they'd never returned to the beautiful white they had been. Now they were a swirl of dingy, greyish- white, and a constant reminder of the injustice in her life. She continued to wear them as a silent act of rebellion against Shelby.

But, for now, she had to stop thinking about this; she would bring this memory back up later when she wanted to taste the bitterness again.

DIGGING DEEPER

The Battle Within: *Bitterness*

Merriam-Webster defines *bitterness* as "distasteful or distressing to the mind."

Tabitha is experiencing bitter feelings from a hurt she received from a past event. Instead of trying to let it go, she thinks about the event over and over. This seems to allow the bitter feelings to remain with her and even grow.

1. Have you ever had anything you dearly loved destroyed on accident or on purpose by someone? How did you feel?

2. If the action was on purpose, have you forgiven them, even if they never asked for forgiveness? How difficult was it to forgive them? Or are you still harboring bitter feelings? If so, is it time to talk with someone about this issue?

**Ephesians 4:31-32 states: *"Let all bitterness and wrath and anger and clamor and slander be put away from you, along with all malice. Be kind to one another, tenderhearted, forgiving one another, as God in Christ forgave you."*

*How can this verse help you work through bitterness?

3. "She felt covered now. And she didn't know how to cut or dig out of the bitterness without causing herself discomfort. She just didn't want to forgive Shelby; it would be too much work for her."

**After reading this quote, what do you think Tabitha means?

YOUR NOTES

BITTERNESS

SIX

ENVY

Still sitting in the dark cave with her hands on her Vans, Tabitha turned her thoughts to her mom and the rest of her family. Tabitha's mom was the one who really knew and understood her, even when she didn't understand herself. Tabby, as her mom called her, was an introvert. Her mom explained that being an introvert was okay; that God had made her that way and had a great plan for her life. He would use her personality and talents to bring Him glory.

Despite what her mom said, Tabitha wanted so much to be like her older sister, Sarah, who was an all-out, fun-loving extrovert. But try as she might, Tabitha couldn't say the right things or be like Sarah. She was so hard to compete with; there really was no competition at all. Sarah was seventeen years old, smart, beautiful, and athletic...and such a nice person. Everyone wanted to be around her. Tabby loved her, but she envied her big sister. In fact, she was even envious of her younger brother, Jacob. Even at five years old, he was making more friends than her. She desperately wanted to spend time with both of them, but the longer she was with them, the meaner she became. She would say hurtful things and give evil glares. The whole time she knew she was wrong for being mean, but she still couldn't stop herself. She loved them completely but didn't know how to tell them.

An event she wished she could erase from history was a time her feelings of envy caused her to hurt her siblings. The junior high and high school students had had a back-to-back award's night. Tabitha knew she would not receive many awards, but she was praying so hard to receive the English award. She had worked extremely hard that year and hoped to be at the top of her class in this subject. When the time came for her teacher to announce the winner, Tabitha's heart was racing, and her palms were sweaty. She closed her eyes and whispered, "Please God, please..." but the name spoken in the microphone was not her own. Her disbelief and disappointment took her breath away.

Sarah knew she'd wanted that award so bad and turned to look at her, with pity in her eyes, and mouthed, "I'm sorry." She didn't want her sister's pity; it felt belittling. Then, the night got a hundred times worse when her sister received several glowing comments and awards from her teachers and coaches. Tabitha couldn't even get one award, but her sister was walking out from the event with her arms full! On the way home, her parents were gushing all over Sarah about her wonderful accomplishments. "Oh, Sarah, your volleyball coach said the kindest words about you…We are so proud of you for getting that History award. We know you worked hard…" Even Jacob was saying how cool she was! All the while, Tabitha was sitting in the back of the van seething. She knew Sarah had worked hard and deserved those awards, but her victories made Tabitha's defeat feel worse.

Once they arrived home, Sarah asked if she could go get some ice cream with her friends to celebrate. When her parents had agreed, Jacob shouted out, "Please, please can I carry your awards to your room?" After Sarah handed him the awards, he carried them very carefully towards the house. Tabitha was so filled with anger and envy she jumped out of the van and ran into the house first. As she stopped at her bedroom doorway, she heard Jacob chatting away to himself, "Sarah is so awesome! Look at these cool awards." As he was about to pass by her to take the awards to Sarah's room, Tabitha let her envy and anger take control. Striking out in a way she still regretted to this day, she'd stuck her foot out just in time to trip Jacob. She could still see the scene like it was in slow motion. Jacob screamed in distress as his body lurched forward. All the awards went flying in the air. They'd hit the wall, bounced on the floor, and then slid a ways. Besides some bruises, Jacob was okay, but Sarah's awards suffered. A couple received scratches and dents, but the volleyball trophy broke into several pieces. As soon as Jacob was consoled, Tabitha immediately felt remorse. She could not believe she had acted that way. She couldn't believe it now.

Tabitha did try in other ways to make up for her meanness and to show she cared. She knew her family well: their loves, their interests. If she ever saw something that reminded her of them, she bought it. Once she bought her mother a dozen chocolate candies that were going out of season because she knew her mother treasured every bite of that special treat. She also loved making crafts, so she would make things for them, like bracelets or bookmarks. And, of course, she would send funny memes or cute emojis to express her love. That might not have been the same as words, but it was all she knew how to do.

Still, Tabitha's mom spent hours talking to her, trying to get her to open up and express her feelings with words. She understood her struggles and wanted Tabitha to understand and recognize them also so she could "turn them over to God and let Him heal her." She would say, "He is the only one that could truly bring you peace and joy."

After the awards event, when she tripped her brother, Tabitha's mother gave her one of her "talks." Her mother walked in the room and in a quiet voice asked, "Why?" That quiet voice always indicated that her mother was extremely upset, and she was trying to keep herself calm and collected. The usual response flew out of Tabitha's mouth, "I don't know." Next came her mom's standard reply, "Well, I'm not leaving until we talk this through and figure out why you acted that way." Her mother asked probing questions like, "How were you feeling when you didn't receive the English award? How were you feeling when Sarah received hers?"and "What were you thinking when you tripped your brother?" The questions finally stopped when Tabitha confessed her true feelings.

Confessing, out loud, the emotions she battled within, always left her feeling exhausted. She loved her mother for trying to help her, but she got so angry with her too. Her mother made getting over a problem sound so easy. She didn't know what it was like being a teenager these days. She didn't know how it felt to be friendless. Her mom was just like her sister when it came to making conversation and friends. So, yes, she always seemed to have the uncanny ability to know what Tabitha was thinking and feeling, but she couldn't truly understand. She was not her!

Her mom was a woman of ideas and actions. Sometimes she was so busy running around and coming up with new plans, that she made Tabitha tired just watching her. She liked the adventures her mom would take her on or even push her into, and she loved that her mom could sense when she had a problem. She would work for hours sometimes to pull the problem out of her.

Then there was her dad. He was a calm presence she appreciated much of the time. Her dad was very much the opposite of her mom, and she loved him for it. Dad was okay with being still and quiet. He was like Tabitha- more reserved, a bit introverted, and he thought long and hard about things before taking action. He even had a quirky sense of humor. She and her dad had many inside jokes that the others in the family did not understand. Tabitha knew she could always sit beside her dad and just 'be.' He didn't understand her either, but he was the steady constant in a whirlwind of chaos. In fact, it was a running joke in the family that Mom was like a kite blowing here and there in the wind, and Dad was the one on the ground holding tight to the string so she wouldn't blow away.

They really were a good pair. Mom needed Dad to slow her down, and Dad needed Mom to speed him up. She was truly thankful for them. She knew many teens her age did not have the blessing of two loving parents. She knew she needed to focus on her blessings, but it was so easy to get her eyes off what God had given her and to look at all the bad things. The negatives in her life always seemed so much bigger than the positives: How she didn't measure up to her siblings. How she couldn't make friends. How she wasn't as pretty, smart, or as skinny as the others at school. How life wasn't fair. Oh, how she wished she could be done with these negative thoughts! She was frightened enough trying to find her way out of this place; she didn't need to be depressed more right now.

Taking out her M&M's and popping a few in her mouth, she knew she had more important things to do. She had to survive! When Tabitha was younger, she used to imagine that the M&M's gave her super strength. She smiled at the memory as she ate a few more and tucked the rest away to begin her crawl. Imagining that the M&M's gave her the power and extra muscle to help her in this next phase of her journey, she stated with determination, "I am going to find my way out to freedom!"

DIGGING DEEPER

The Battle Within: *Envy*

Merriam-Webster defines *envy* as "painful or resentful awareness of an advantage enjoyed by another joined with a desire to possess the same advantage."

Envy can take your thoughts and eyes off your blessings and gifts, making you focus on what others have and what you lack.

1. Do you have feelings of envy towards anyone, whether a family member or a friend?

Read Proverbs 14:30 (ESV), "A tranquil [healing] heart gives life to the flesh, but envy makes the bones rot."

Wow! This Bible verse really draws a picture of the effects of envy. Just like Tabitha's mom's tree was close to dying and would eventually rot away, envy, like bitterness, can do that to us. Take the time now to confess your envious feelings to God; then ask Him to heal your heart and help you be content with yourself. God does not make mistakes. You are His beautiful creation, and He has a wonderful plan for your life now and forever.

2. If you do find yourself falling back into envious or negative thoughts instead of focusing on your blessings, remember Psalm 103:2, "Bless the LORD, O my soul, and forget not all his benefits…" Take the time to write down all your blessings, big and small.

3. If you have a close relationship with your parents, talk with them. If not, is there someone else you can talk to (a family member, grandparent, sibling, pastor, or teacher)? Find that trusted person and share your struggles. Ask them to keep you accountable to focusing on your blessings instead of the negatives.

4. Just for fun: do you have a childhood memory like Tabitha's of the M&M's that gave her super strength? Share.

YOUR NOTES

SEVEN

ANGER

Tabitha slowly started to baby crawl towards the big openness ahead. A few feet in, so far so good; a few feet more, and her hand felt the rock wall. So, okay; no open pit, but after feeling around some more, she realized there were two openings. Two tunnels perhaps? Which one should she take? Would both lead her out? Or would one lead her to a pit of vipers that she desperately wanted to avoid?

Taking out her water bottle from the side pocket of her backpack, she took a big gulp and contemplated which way to go. Then, out of all things to pop in her head was the song, "Backpack, backpack..." from *Dora the Explorer*. Oh boy; was she losing it? The *Wonder Pets* theme song began playing in her head next. "Wonder pets, wonder pets, we're on our way...." When her brother was younger, she used to love to watch him standing in front of the t.v. shaking his little bottom back and forth while he sang that song. Then, if he saw her in the room, he would grab her hand, pull her to the t.v. and make her dance and sing along with him. Giving in to the sweet memory and the silliness that exhaustion can bring, she started singing out loud and just decided to head to the left. Left was good. And now that she could feel the rock walls on both sides, she decided to walk instead of crawl but still go slowly just in case...

After singing her childhood cartoon songs, she switched to some doom and gloom songs. She realized the songs were making her fear worse, so she switched to happier ones. A few songs in, it dawned on her that singing as she walked actually helped her forget the darkness and fear of the unknown. Whatever song popped in her mind, she would sing. Ten songs later, she was moving on to her own Tabitha-style remix songs. Bobbing her head singing, "Dum Dum, diddy dum dum," she had forgotten about her fear, until she heard a noise.

She halted and turned her ear to the noise, trying to decipher what it was. Lava boiling? Snakes hissing? Bats flapping their wings? A bear chomping his teeth ready for a Tabby snack? Plop, plop, plop. Was it just water dripping? Hoping against all hope that it was, she ceased her singing, concentrating more on each downward step. She noticed that the walls were becoming wetter. Despite her caution, her feet suddenly went out from under her, and she started sliding. She was screaming. Her hands tried to grasp at anything that would stop her roller coaster ride. To no avail. She could not stop herself. Soon, she found the end. She landed in a shallow pool of water.

Jumping up out of the cold water, she opened her eyes to a glorious sight – light! She could see! Was she free? Had she finally found the way out? Screaming for help, she frantically looked around for a way out, but her moment of optimism burst like a bubble when she saw no opening for escape. Instead, her eyes travelled up to the source of light where she saw a small crack in the tall ceiling of the cave. She felt distressed because she'd hit another dead end. There was some relief though because she could see. The stream of light was such a beautiful sight for Tabitha. For a moment, she stood face up, staring at the light and basking in that small ray. Looking around again, to actually take in everything, she could finally see colors, the walls, cool stalactites she had only learned about in books, her bloody hands, her torn clothing, the water pool she was standing knee deep in, her starry night backpack. Oh no! The backpack! Did it get soaked through when she landed in the water? Did her precious items get ruined?

Grabbing the bag, she breathed a sigh of relief. Thankfully, her backpack landed front side down in the water, so her journal, book, and Bible had not gotten wet. Well, her tissues were a nasty wad, but everything else was safe. Pulling all the items out to let them dry a bit, she felt and heard her stomach speak, and the nuts and M&M's called her name.

Since she was taking a small break to reassess her situation, and there was a little light, she decided to look at her journal to maybe jog her memory. When she opened the journal, a letter fell out. Picking it up, she saw her name written on the front in her mother's handwriting.

At that moment EVERYTHING from the last couple of days came back to her. Tabitha's parents had left this note beside her bed to help prepare her for the meeting that morning. The meeting where Tabitha would have to apologize to someone who she did not like at all. Someone who had been a thorn in her side. Shelby!

Thinking back to the beginning of school, she knew the exact moment she'd become Shelby's enemy. The moment that would start months of misery for Tabitha, was the first week of school, the last class of the day- English. The teacher had put the students in groups of six to discuss the book, The Witch of

ANGER

Blackbird Pond, *which they were to have read over the summer. Shelby was new to the school, having just moved to town. Tabitha did not know Shelby hadn't read the book. As they started discussing Katherine Tyler, the main character who lived with some Puritan relatives, Shelby chimed in asking, "Did that mean they couldn't use electricity and Wifi?" Tabitha, excited about discussing the book, thought she was making a joke and replied in the same manner, "Yeah; can you believe they didn't have those things in the 1600s?" This, of course, humiliated Shelby; especially when the group started giggling. Her face turned red, and the glare she gave Tabitha sent chills down her spine, telling her revenge was coming. Tabitha knew she needed to talk to Shelby to say she was sorry, to explain she didn't mean it the way it sounded, but she just couldn't build up enough courage. She chickened out, which caused her more problems to come. From that day on, Shelby sought every opportunity to treat Tabitha with malice and point out her flaws to others, even going as far as using social media.*

Tabitha did her best to ignore the comments and anger she was feeling. Though, as time went on, each hurtful word, evil glare, or sarcastic laugh directed towards her started to fuel the anger, like throwing wood on a small fire. When Shelby ruined her shoes, it set her anger blazing. She couldn't ignore it any longer. At first, her angry feelings caused her to lash out at her family. She could recall the many times she'd yelled at her brother to leave her alone, when all he wanted to do was sit beside her and watch t.v., calling her sister ugly names, when she was only trying to give her helpful advice, or telling her parents she hated them and running to her room and slamming the door. Once, she even hit the bathroom wall out of anger. She knew she was hurting others and even herself. She had to do something. She just didn't know what that was.

Fast forward to this past Monday...she had finally had enough. Tabitha had pushed down her hurt and anger towards Shelby. She had bottled it up, and now felt she would explode. It reminded her of an experiment they'd done in class long ago. The teacher put Mentos in a bottle of soda pop, and all the contents exploded out of the top with such force. She felt like that. She knew she should have been talking to her parents or someone about her feelings and what was happening. She just never knew how to start the conversation. So, she held it in, or at times, the feelings would leak out on her family. Those would be the times she struck out at them in anger. Now, she couldn't handle it anymore, and it was time to do something to get back at Shelby. Tabitha wanted Shelby to feel at least a little of the hurt she had been feeling. She knew her opportunity for revenge had come on Monday afternoon when her English teacher announced that they had a short story assignment due that following Friday.

Tabitha was still not good at confrontation or 'comebacks' in an argument, but she thought this short story would be a great way to strike at Shelby.

That Friday, they were to read their stories in front of the whole class. She worked all week to word the story just right. Finally, Friday arrived. When it was Tabitha's turn, she walked up, with a little fear rippling through her body, but she also felt like she was going into a battle. With her weapon drawn–the written word-her story, she was ready to strike her enemy. She had spent many days preparing for this battle. She was ready to defeat the enemy, but at the same time, she kept feeling this uneasiness, like maybe she shouldn't do this. This feeling of trepidation was always nagging her. Every time she started to really explore the feeling, she would think about something Shelby had done to her, and she would push that uneasiness away. Despite that little war inside her, she finished the story.

The short story was all about a beautiful young girl that had to serve a nasty, evil, and ugly girl troll. This troll was able to disguise herself under a magical outfit that made her look like a pretty princess and deceive all those around her; especially the handsome prince. This troll hated the beautiful young girl and did everything she could to try to destroy her life. One day, the young girl was able to pull the magical outfit off the troll, right in front of the prince. The prince's eyes were opened to the real beauty in the room–the young girl. He was completely disgusted and angered by the troll, so he sent her to live under the town's bridge and work the remainder of her ugly life. To pass over the bridge, the village people had to yell out the ugly troll's name. Tabitha paused at this point in the story. She took a dramatic pause just to make sure everyone was listening. Without looking up, she started reading again with all the boldness she'd ever possessed... "So not only did the mean troll girl have to work hard, but she had to be humiliated hourly by hearing her name shouted by the villagers, "Ugly Shelly, Ugly Shelly, get off your jelly belly, and open the gate!"

No; the name of the troll was not Shelby, but by all the gasps she heard escape the mouths of her classmates, she knew they understood who she was referring to; especially Shelby.

After completing her revenge, she sat down ready to bask in her victory, to taste the sweetness of hurting Shelby. That nasty girl deserved it. But strangely, Tabitha didn't feel very victorious. She felt this pit in her stomach. She felt sick like she had been on too many roller coasters after eating too many hot dogs. Tabitha glanced over at Shelby in hopes to see her with her head down on her desk in shame. Shelby was not cowering in her seat or holding her hand over her heart, conveying she was so sorry for all that she had done to Tabitha. No; Shelby was waiting for Tabitha to look at her. She was staring her down, willing Tabitha to look at her. Shelby was seething and boiling with anger. Yes; her eyes were watery with unshed tears, but those tears did not dare spill over. If they had, the tears would have evaporated quickly due to the heat of anger radiating off Shelby's cheeks. Then her lips whispered to Tabitha, "I hate you."

Tabitha knew the battle had not ended but was an all-out war now. She had not defeated the enemy. She'd made things worse. That revenge she thought would be the best thing in the world became the actual worst feeling she had ever felt. The funny thing was, if Shelby had been sorry, Tabitha would still have felt the same. She felt truly ugly and dirty from the inside out, like the troll in her story. She was so ashamed of what she had done. She knew better. Her father had always told her, "Two wrongs do not make a right." She knew both her mother and father had taught her that God would judge the sins of others.

Thinking back over the story, she couldn't believe she had written or much less read it. So why did she do this? How had she let things get so bad... go this far?

DIGGING DEEPER

The Battle Within: *Anger*

Merriam-Webster defines *anger* as "a strong feeling of displeasure and usually of antagonism."

Anger is a powerful emotion. Feelings of anger can spring up suddenly, or like a simmering pot of water, anger can be felt for a long time. Left unchecked, this emotion can cause so much pain and destruction. Tabitha had been feeling anger towards Shelby for several months. She eventually let her anger boil over and caused Shelby and herself hurt.

1. Have you ever tried to make a joke that hurt someone's feelings? Did you immediately apologize? If not, why? Should you now?

2. Have you ever experienced a time you felt you wanted revenge? Why is getting revenge wrong? Does it really help either parties involved? After Tabitha got her revenge, why do you think she didn't feel better?

*If you are struggling with answering the question, read Romans 12:17-21 (ESV): *"Repay no one evil for evil, but give thought to do what is honorable in the sight of all. If possible, so far as it depends on you, live peaceably with all. Beloved, never avenge yourselves, but leave it to the wrath of God, for it* *is written, 'Vengeance is mine, I will repay, says the Lord.' To the contrary, 'if your enemy is hungry, feed him; if he is thirsty, give him something to drink; for by so doing you will heap burning coals on his head.' Do not be overcome by evil, but overcome evil with good."*

3. Why should Tabitha have spoken to her parents or another trusted adult about her feelings of anger and what Shelby was doing? Why do you think she didn't talk to someone?

4. What was the uneasiness Tabitha was feeling while she was writing the short story?

5. What should Tabitha do now now that she has chosen the wrong action?

According to 1 John 1:9 (ESV): *"If we confess our sins, he is faithful and just to forgive us our sins and to cleanse us from all unrighteousness."*

YOUR NOTES

ANGER

EIGHT

SHAME

After she read the story and sat down, thankfully, the end of school bell rang. Grabbing her backpack and keeping her head down, Tabitha ran to the bus and hid herself in the seat right behind the bus driver. She kept her eyes downcast and didn't even allow herself the comfort of reading a book. She needed to sit, think, and feel. As soon as she got home, she took one look in her mother's eyes and confessed everything she'd done. Without being able to hold back her feelings, the words vomited out, "I'm horrible inside and out! I wrote this mean story to try to humiliate Shelby in front of everybody...," between her sobs and walking around the room she continued, "...to try and make her feel as bad as she has made me feel the last several months...to even make the teacher and the others in class see the truth about her...to make them turn their backs on her...I wanted revenge..." Using her shirt to wipe her eyes and nose, she half cried, half whispered, "Instead I feel so horrible and dirty...and now I know how ugly I can be. I knew I shouldn't do it, but I just couldn't stop by myself." Finally, throwing herself on the couch, face down on a pillow, she wailed, "Why, didn't I stop myself?! Why?!" The ugliness of her actions and how she saw herself was all out now.

Sitting in the cave, reliving that shameful moment, made her feel overwhelmed by guilt again. She'd known better than to act like that. Revenge never solved a problem. It only made it worse. With the feelings of shame fresh in her thoughts, another memory, but this time of love from her mother, flooded her mind.

Tabitha's mother listened with patience, compassion, and sadness on her face. Her mother surprised her by first stating that she loved her. "Oh, Tabby, my girl. I love you so much, and it hurts me to know you have been carrying this pain around. I want you to know that I'm here for you always, not just to help, but to listen too. You mean so much to me." Yes; she knew her mother loved her...but it still took her aback. It was easy to love someone when they were loving, kind, and obedient, but to love someone when they had done something so spiteful, evil, ugly, revengeful? She didn't love herself at the moment, so how could her mother love her? But there was the love...she could see it in her mother's eyes. She could feel it while being hugged tightly, her mother absorbing all of her raging emotions, the sobs, the wet, hot tears, and the runny nose that was getting all over her favorite blue shirt.

Her mother was heartbroken over the pain Tabitha had experienced in silence over the hurt Shelby had inflicted. Tabitha knew part of that was her own fault. She had only shared a little with her family over the past months. She was too embarrassed to tell her mother and father all she had been through. She didn't want them to think she was weak or even believe the things Shelby was saying and writing about her. And she didn't want to admit any sin that was her own in this whole thing. Plus, she hated all the conflict. She thought, if her parents knew, then the situation would get even worse. She knew her parents would get the school and Shelby's parents involved. She did not want more attention drawn to her.

Tabitha's mother did admit that she was upset and sad about the way Tabitha had acted. She stated matter-of-factly that Tabitha knew what she was doing was wrong but did it anyway...that was a blatant sin. She reminded her that James 4:17 states, "So whoever knows the right thing to do and fails to do it, for him it is sin," and that thankfully, God is full of grace, mercy, and forgiveness. Tabitha would need to apologize to God and Shelby for the wrong she had done. There were always consequences to sin. The consequence-the punishment would be facing Shelby and apologizing. She would also have to write another short story over the weekend and ask the teacher if she could read it on Monday. This story was not to include "Ugly Shelly;" rather, have only a positive and an uplifting storyline. After the way Tabitha was feeling about reading the first story, she was more than prepared to write another story to right her wrong.

Her mom went to her desk drawer and got out a blank journal. She asked Tabitha to go to her room, to spend time in prayer, to write down all of her feelings, to write out her desires and prayers to God. Later, she and her parents would have a meeting to discuss their game plan for Tabitha's apology, and then figure out how to deal with the trouble Shelby was making for her at school.

Tabitha did not have that prayer journal with her, but she could remember some of what she wrote. She had sat for a long time just staring at the blank page, with her mind racing in different directions. For some reason, she couldn't nail down everything in a nice prayer. Finally, she just wrote down the emotions she was feeling right then.

I feel...
>Shameful
>Sorry, *but still angry at Shelby*
>Tired
>Sad
>Lonely

Then the only prayer that could express her true desire was short and sweet:

"God, help me figure out what is wrong with me!"

That had been her prayer. She just wanted to figure out how to control herself and all the emotions that were raging inside her. She was just tired of the battle.

DIGGING DEEPER

The Battle Within: *Shame*

Merriam-Webster defines *shame* as "a painful emotion caused by consciousness of guilt, shortcoming..."

Tabitha was feeling a lot of shame over the story she wrote and read about Shelby. Dwelling in feelings of shame and guilt for a long time can be damaging. If not dealt with, those feelings can become like a huge weight around your ankles, dragging you down. Talking through these feelings and seeking forgiveness for a wrong action, can release that weight. Tabitha took the first step in confessing to her mom all that had happened.

1. Were you surprised Tabitha's Mother still loved her even after she confessed her sin?

Her mother loved Tabitha despite her mistakes. Her love is a wonderful picture of God's love. It is important to remember her mother is only human and imperfect. In contrast, God is completely perfect, and His love is never-ending towards His children. We can't fully understand how much He loves us. God's love is AMAZING!

Read the verses below and really think about the greatness of God's love:

*Romans 5:8 states, *"God shows His love for us in that while we were still sinners, Christ died for us."*

*Ephesians 3:17-19: *"So that Christ may dwell in your hearts through faith—that you, being rooted and grounded in love, may have strength to comprehend with all the saints what is the breadth and length and height and depth, and to know the love of Christ that surpasses knowledge, that you may be filled with all the fullness of God."*

2. Look at James 4:17 again: *"So, whoever knows the right thing to do and fails to do it, for him it is sin."*

Think about a time or times in your life when you have done something you knew was wrong and did it anyway. Did you ask for forgiveness? If not, this is a perfect time to do just that.

3. What would be the benefit of praying during times like Tabitha is experiencing, or even writing down your prayers, thoughts, and feelings in a journal?

YOUR NOTES

SHAME

NINE

DREAD

Tabitha had her head on her knees whispering the same prayer she had written in the journal, "God, help me figure out what is wrong with me." Making herself continue to remember the events that led to her situation now, she thought back to the plan of action she had made with her parents the night before.

After dinner, her parents sat with Tabitha on her bed. Her dad wanted to pray before they started the game plan. With his deep voice and always right-to-the-point words, he prayed, "God, we thank You for being our Perfect Father and Counselor. You already know the problems Tabitha is facing and the pain she has endured. Please guide her and us right now as to how to deal with these issues. We love you. In the name of Jesus, amen."

Following the prayer and some more discussion, they made a plan. It was not one that Tabitha was excited about but something she knew had to be done. Her parents would go to the school on Monday morning to talk with the principal about the situation between Shelby and Tabitha. Her parents stated that there was definitely no room for bullying–at school or on social media. This had to be resolved quickly. They told her they would not let their daughter continue to suffer in this area, but Tabitha also had to do something very difficult. She had to do what Jesus would want her to do. First, she needed to apologize to Shelby for writing and reading that short story. According to Shelby's social media, she would be at the park for the Saturday soccer rec games. Tabitha and her family would go to the park, and Tabitha would apologize to Shelby face to face. The second part of the plan would be working on forgiving Shelby... even if Shelby never admitted her wrong or said she was sorry. Her dad said, if she could forgive and let go, the burden of bitterness would be released off her shoulders, and she could walk lighter again. Third, she would help her mother remove the ivy from the choking tree in their backyard. Her parents thought this would be a perfect object lesson for dealing with her bitterness.

Tabitha had a restless night with little sleep. She tossed, turned, and beat her pillows, just like the pounding that was going on in her head with her emotions of shame, anger, sadness, bitterness, and fear. She was having such a difficult time coming to terms with Shelby and everything that had happened over the last few months. One moment, she would be ready to forgive; then, the next moment, a memory of Shelby making fun of her would pop in her mind. Then, she would bathe in that bitterness until she tried to pull herself back to what she knew was right.

The next morning, she woke to her alarm going off, playing an up-beat happy song that made her groan out loud. She was not in the mood to be cheerful. She had chosen this song in hopes it would help motivate her to have the right mindset for the events ahead. Well, fat chance of that! She was only feeling dread. Reaching to turn off the alarm, she saw a letter. She immediately knew it was from her parents. They'd learned, over the years, that the written word meant so much to her. Sometimes she could learn more about a lesson from reading it rather than listening to another lecture. Tabitha opened the letter and began reading,

Dear Tabby,

You are so precious to us. When we held you in our arms for the first time and looked into your brilliant blue eyes, we knew God had graced us with such a treasure and beauty. We prayed you would become a young lady who loves God with your whole heart and displays His love in everything you do, just like your namesake in the Bible (Acts 9:36-42). Tabitha, you are not perfect, as are none of us.

But the important thing is trying your best. If you trust in God, focus on pleasing Him, even in times of failure or through difficulty, you will grow stronger in Him. That is the Christian walk. We are learning to be more like Jesus by God's refining and shaping of us. Coming to us last night showed maturity. You recognized and confessed your sin and then decided to apologize to someone that has caused you a lot of pain.

Oh, how we wish we could save you from any hurt or pain. Please know; When you are hurting, we are too. We love you so very much. But life is difficult, and we are not only battling our own selves but also the devil and his evil forces working through people. You are going to have struggles your whole life. These struggles will be painful at times, but they can make you stronger if you trust in God and allow Him to guide you. He has given us all the equipment we need (Ephesians 6:10-18) for these battles. When you use this equipment, joined with constant prayer, then you will be able to handle all the battles that come into your life, despite the pain. But you have to put on the armor.

A Christian's identity is defined by Christ who lives in her. A Christian can walk holding her head high because she is a child of THE King. God loves His children and gives them victory in Him. There is no need to cower behind fear of rejection, or to worry about what others might say, or to focus on negative things that have happened in the past. There is no need to worry about what could happen or blame others for unhappiness.

Tabitha, we pray you understand, believe, and will:

Fasten that **belt of truth** around your waist. Read His Word, and learn more about who you are in Him–the truth.

Put on the **breastplate of righteousness**. This will enable you to live and walk in the right way, as taught in His Word.

Place those cool, high-top **shoes of peace** on your feet, so you can stand strong in the midst of turmoil, knowing He will keep you stable. And also, use those shoes of peace to bring His Good News to others.

Hang on tight to that **shield of faith**, so you can block the darts of hurtful words and actions the devil is going to try to throw at you.

Place that **helmet of salvation** on your head. Jesus died on a cross to take your sins upon Himself and to save you from eternal punishment. He also wants to save you daily from negative and damaging thoughts that will try to enter your head and tear you apart. Protect your brain with His saving truth. Think on His blessings and all the positives around you.

Then, raise your **sword of God's Word**. His truth and love will fight for you.

Talk with Him every day, and listen. God will be with you each step of the way, guiding and directing.

So Daughter, suit up, and pray up, so you will be prepared for the task in front of you today.

Tabby, Our Girl, know we are proud of you, love you greatly and pray for you daily.

Love,
Dad and Mom

Wiping some escaped tears off her cheeks, she folded the letter and tucked it in her journal and put it in her backpack. She so loved her parents for caring. She knew the words in the letter were true, but right now, she just couldn't focus. She should take the time to pray, but she was so nervous about the apology. She just wanted to leave right now and get the whole thing over with. Then, maybe she could take some time later to pray and ask God to help her from now on. Grabbing her backpack, she called out to her parents that she was ready to go and would be waiting in the van.

The ride to the park felt like it would never end. The usual fifteen-minute drive felt like hours. She could hear drums playing in her head, like she was being escorted to her death. She kept reminding herself: at least after her talk with Shelby, she could console herself in the library next to the park. The library felt like her second home. In fact, the whole area was a special place. The library and park were next to a state forest. She and her family had spent many hours enjoying the facilities, having picnics together, and walking the trails. This place was beautiful and peaceful. The library, though, was her favorite. It was a place where she could relax in a quiet corner and escape in a book, into another world where the heroes fought brave battles and won against evil.

Arriving at the park, her siblings went ahead to the library, while her parents walked with her to the field to confront Shelby. As she started walking, she began thinking about what it would look like to have her parents with her. She would look like a baby needing to hold her parents' hands. She needed to do this apology thing on her own. So, she made a decision that started sweat dripping under her arms. Turning to her parents, she pleaded, "Can I please do this on my own? You can just wait for me in the library. It isn't far away. Plus, I think I would look really lame if you were with me. Since I have to do this, I don't want my daddy and mommy by my side. Please?" With a lot of hesitation, they finally agreed. They told her again that they loved her and were proud she was doing this.

After Tabitha saw her parents disappear into the sliding doors of the library, she reluctantly started walking towards the soccer field. She easily identified Shelby beside the bleachers, soccer ball under one arm and Gatorade in her other hand, talking and laughing with her friends. Tabitha approached the group with such fear, she knew everyone around her had to feel it radiating off her.

Shelby looked up and immediately stopped laughing, her face turning like stone. She spat out in anger, "What are you doing here?"

Knowing, if she did not speak now, she might chicken out and run the other way, she quickly said, "Shelby, I want to say sorry for the story I wrote about you and read to the class. It was wrong and mean, and I hope you can forgive me." As the last words left her mouth, she had to take a deep breath to refill her empty lungs. Tabitha knew she had taken Shelby by surprise. She also knew by looking at her, Shelby felt no forgiveness towards her.

Shelby looked at her group of friends, laughed sarcastically and said, "Can you believe this?" Looking back at Tabitha, with eyes that seemed to shoot out fire, she said matter-of-factly, "I will never forgive you and will always hate you." Then, with an evil laugh, threw out, "And you better watch your back because you never know what could happen."

Tabitha knew nothing more could be done, so she turned to walk away. Even though Shelby had not received her apology with kindness, Tabitha felt instant relief. The humiliating moment was over. She felt the huge weight was gone. Now she could move on and try to control herself more in the future. And just maybe, Shelby would eventually change and be kind to her.

Walking away, a smile sprang to her lips, as she felt hope rising within her. Tabitha started to text her parents saying all was good, and she was on her way, when she felt a ball hit the back of her head. The hit jolted her body forward, causing her to trip, drop her phone and fall to her knees. Touching her head, she turned around to see Shelby and the group of girls laughing.

Then Shelby yelled in a sugary sweet voice, "Oh, I'm so sorry. Will you ever forgive me?"

The hope she had felt rising within, now fell hard, along with her pride. As she stood up and grabbed her phone, she could hear the shrilling laughter exploding from the mouths of Shelby and her friends. She glanced back quickly to see them all fist bumping in congratulations.

All she could think to do was run away and run away fast. She took off near a trail and ran and ran, feeling the embarrassment and shame following her. Not watching where she was going, running and using her right hand to stop the branches from slapping her face, just like Shelby's hatred and rejection did, she tripped over a root and fell.

DIGGING DEEPER

The Battle Within: *Dread*

Merriam-Webster defines *dread* as "to fear greatly or to feel extreme reluctance to meet or face."

Tabitha was filled with dread over facing Shelby and apologizing. The confrontation required her to humble herself, to admit a wrong, and to face someone who had shown no compassion in the past.

1. How would you have felt minutes before approaching Shelby?

2. How did you feel after Shelby struck out at Tabitha again?

3. Do you think Tabitha was correct in telling her parents about the bullying? Do you think their involvement will help the situation?

4. What did you think about the letter Tabitha's parents wrote? How was the letter encouraging and helpful? As you think through this question, consider Proverbs 1:8-9 (ESV): *"Hear, my son, your father's instruction, and forsake not your mother's teaching, for they are a graceful garland for your head and pendants for your neck"*

5. After reading her parents' letter, what should Tabitha have done? Did she "suit up" in the armor of God that her parents mentioned?

YOUR NOTES

DREAD

TEN

ENLIGHTENMENT

Tabitha felt exhausted, sitting in the cave, reliving all that had happened that morning. How could one girl be so mean? Why did Shelby want to continue to hurt her? Was Tabitha that bad a person? Did no one want to give her a chance? Oh, how she wished she could just shake Shelby and make her see who she was; to make her want to be nice to her. Tabitha just wanted to understand why Shelby acted like she did. She wished she could understand why she, herself, had acted the way *she* did. Why were her feelings so up and down like a seesaw? She couldn't control Shelby or others, but she should at least be able to control herself.

"Why? Why? WHY?" she yelled out.

The whole memory made her feel so many emotions. They were battling from the inside out. She bounced from sadness to anger to shame to frustration to fear to worry…she was so tired of the war. How could her emotions have so much control over her? It seemed they moved back and forth like a pinball in her brain. This pinball would hit the switches to different emotions and change her mood without any warning. It was like she was at the mercy of whatever emotion decided to take over her mind, and then she would do whatever she felt at that moment. Her thoughts, words, facial expressions, and actions were all controlled by what she felt. Most of the time she knew when she was acting, thinking, or saying the wrong things, but she didn't know how to stop herself. She wanted to be able to control herself; especially around people like Shelby, but how?

She remembered some verses that always seemed to be in the back of her mind; verses she had never fully understood. They were from the book of Romans, written by a man named Paul. At first, Paul hated Christians and persecuted them. Then, through a miraculous encounter with Jesus, Paul became a Christian himself. He wrote many of the books of the New Testament. He was way too smart for her, and sometimes it was difficult to understand some of what he wrote. She did know that in chapter 7, he wrote something she could relate to.

Feeling like her life depended on it, she took out her Bible to search for the verses. Starting at the beginning of chapter 7, she finally found the section at verse 15, "For I do not understand my own actions. For I do not do what I want, but I do the very thing I hate." That was how she felt. She knew what was right. She just couldn't seem to do it. And Paul continued to explain that he was battling himself and the sin that lived inside him, and Jesus was the only one who could save him from this battle.

For a long time, Tabitha believed she was God's girl. She thought she was saved and in His family. She grew up in church. She knew the Bible stories and all the right answers to the teachers' questions. She had heard how to be saved over and over and knew the words she needed to say. She even remembered saying those words. It was two years ago at a Vacation Bible School. She had had such a fun week with her friends. She had enjoyed playing the games, making the crafts, and learning about the cool Bible stories. On the last night after singing and listening to the lesson about God's great love, the teacher asked, "Do any of you want to be saved and live in Heaven one day with God? If so, raise your hand." Tabitha had glanced over and saw several of her friends raise their hands. She wanted to live in Heaven with God; especially since her friends wanted to also, so she proudly raised her hand. Then, the teacher had those who raised their hands recite a prayer after her. Tabitha repeated the words the teacher said. Afterwards, there were many hugs, smiles, and congratulations from friends and family. The following week, her mother had given her the Bible that said, "God's Girl." It was such a good memory…until now.

Tabitha realized now that the words she recited in that prayer, two years ago, were just words. She had not honestly meant them. She only repeated the words because her friends were doing it, and who wouldn't want to live in Heaven one day? She had felt happiness because others were happy. Soon, though, that feeling of happiness had worn off. There was no real change within her. Yes, she continued to go to church, to do the things she was supposed to, but there was no real passion or joy in those actions.

Right there, in the dim cave, God showed her the truth. Tabitha had never truly believed in Jesus as her Savior. She'd never confessed her sins or given her life to Jesus. With her heart pounding, she sensed this awakening, this draw, to make her really look at herself.

Tabitha, with her imaginative mind, pictured herself collapsed on the dirty ground in the dark, alone, downcast, and burdened. Her clothes were ripped and torn, covered in dirt. This covering of dirt was actually her own sins. Lifting her head slightly, due to the heaviness of her shame, she could see a light far off in the distance. This light was God holding His arms outstretched to her. She yearned to run to Him, but there was a great divide between them. There was no way she could reach Him on her own; especially with her sins weighing her down.

For the first time, all her sins—all the bad things she had thought, said, and done—made her heart really ache with pain, sadness, and regret. This heartache was not for herself but for the One against whom she had sinned …God. He had created her in love, but she had rejected Him through her sins.

Jesus' death became personal to her now. Before, she'd only thought in broad terms, that Jesus had paid for the sins of the "whole world". Tabitha had detached herself from the event. Now, it was more personal. Instead of thinking of the horrible sins committed by others, she saw her sin. Tabitha saw Jesus bearing her sins and taking her punishment. Each slash of the whip on His body, each thorn pushed in His head, each pounding of the nails deeper in is His hands and feet, each excruciating breath He tried to take while hanging on the cross, each drop of blood poured out until He finally died, was a result of her sin, her disobedience against the Holy God who created her. Jesus did not commit her sins, but He willingly took the punishment for them.

Oh; her heart ached to imagine what pain He'd endured. It wasn't just the physical pain, but also the weight of all her sins and the separation from His Father that Jesus felt during that time. Jesus suffered and died because God asked Him to and because of the GREAT love He had for her.

At that moment, Tabitha knew, without a doubt, that she wanted to be in God's family, His girl. She wanted to give her whole self to Him. With a God-given confidence, she prayed simply but in complete sincerity, "God, I believe in You and Your son, Jesus. Thank You, Jesus, for dying for all my ugly sins. I'm so, so very sorry for my sins. And thank You for coming back to life three days later and defeating my sin, the devil, and death. I don't deserve Your love and forgiveness, but I'm so thankful for it! Please help me live for You. Thank you for being my Father and accepting me as Your daughter. Amen."

She could not hear a loud chorus singing, "Hallelujah" or see a great light shining on her like someone might imagine in a movie. Instead, she sensed a peace that came to rest in her heart. In her mind, she pictured, again, that great divide separating her from God and His outstretched arms. She saw Jesus come and pick her up off the dirty ground. With a loving hand, Jesus lifted her down-trodden face and looked at her with a huge smile on His. He replaced her dirty and torn clothing with clean white clothes. Then, putting Her hand in His, they walked bravely over the great divide, on the very cross of Jesus, to the embrace of God's loving arms. She left that old sinful self behind and now was a new creation.

She knew she was not yet in Heaven with God, but she felt that now she truly was God's girl!

She also knew that even though she was God's girl, it did not mean she was perfect or that life would be perfect. "Just like Paul, I'm going to battle myself and my sin. I'm going to have to battle the world and the devil. He is going to try to distract me from focusing on God and the good things God has for my life." As Tabitha spoke these words to herself, her voice grew with confidence. "I'm going to have these battles all my life, until I'm in Heaven with a perfect body. And God, thank You that I don't have to fight alone!" Like a flick of a light switch, Bible verses that she had memorized started to flood her mind, reminding her of just that! God said He would be with her…He had a plan for her…

Suddenly, Tabitha felt hungry. Not hungry for food, but to learn more about what she seemed to be missing. Forgetting that she was sitting in a cave with only a little light, she picked up her parents' letter, wanting to reread what they had told her. She realized she had missed so much the first time. Now some of the things they'd written were jumping out at her, begging for her to understand. And this time, she decided to actually read the Bible verses they had written and really drink it all in.

She wanted to start with her namesake, Tabitha, that her parents mentioned in their letter. She knew the story well, but she wanted to read it again through her new outlook as a child of God. Picking up the Bible, she turned to Acts 9:36-42 and read aloud,

"Now there was in Joppa a disciple named Tabitha, which, translated, means Dorcas. She was full of good works and acts of charity. In those days she became ill and died, and when they had washed her, they laid her in an upper room. Since Lydda was near Joppa, the disciples, hearing that Peter was there, sent two men to him, urging him, 'Please come to us without delay.' So, Peter rose and went with them. And when he arrived, they took him to the upper room. All the widows stood beside him weeping and showing tunics and other garments that Dorcas made while she was with them. But Peter put them all outside, and knelt down and prayed; and turning to the body he said, "Tabitha, arise." And she opened her eyes, and when she saw Peter she sat up. And he gave her his hand and raised her up. Then, calling the saints and widows, he presented her alive. And it became known throughout all Joppa, and many believed in the Lord."

ENLIGHTENMENT

She knew Tabitha had been a follower of Jesus and did "good works" and showed love. Until now, she'd never thought about how Tabitha was first named a disciple, and then the Bible mentioned her being "full of good works and acts of charity." Maybe there was no big significance, but in this moment, that part was speaking to her. She knew she needed to improve on doing good things and showing love for others, but before that, she needed others to see her as a disciple of Jesus. Now she knew she needed to work on her relationship with Jesus—learn more about Him, grow more in Him—so that when she started doing good works, others will know it is because of Him. That was what really mattered. Not praise or others liking her for what she did, but pointing others to Jesus. She whispered in the quietness of her heart. "Jesus, please help me to know and love You more."

Then she moved on to her parents' advice and direction from the Ephesians 6 verses about the Armor of God. She had read these verses a lot about the Armor of God and had even acted them out in a drama for Sunday school. But honestly, she'd never really seen past the dress up and play acting. She'd never seen this as something she should really do. Was there really some truth about putting on these pieces of armor? With her parents' explanation of the verses in the back of her mind, Tabitha read the Bible verses with a fresh new eye.

"Finally, be strong in the Lord and in the strength of his might. Put on the whole armor of God, that you may be able to stand against the schemes of the devil. For we do not wrestle against flesh and blood, but against the rulers, against the authorities, against the cosmic powers over this present darkness, against the spiritual forces of evil in the heavenly places. Therefore, take up the whole armor of God, that you may be able to withstand in the evil day, and having done all, to stand firm. Stand therefore, having fastened on the belt of truth, and having put on the breastplate of righteousness, and, as shoes for your feet, having put on the readiness given by the gospel of peace. In all circumstances, take up the shield of faith, with which you can extinguish all the flaming darts of the evil one; and take the helmet of salvation, and the sword of the Spirit, which is the word of God, praying at all times in the Spirit, with all prayer and supplication." (Ephesians 6:10-18)

After rereading the armor Bible verses and her mom and dad's comments once again, it was like the light streaming in from the cave ceiling shone a spotlight on her actions and attitude from this morning. She knew this "light" could only have come from God. He was helping her understand what she'd done wrong after waking up this morning. Tabitha had never "suited up." She'd never truly stopped to pray and ask God to fight this battle for her. She hadn't studied His Word or really thought about His Truth. Because of this lack of preparation, she'd gone into the situation unprepared and really vulnerable. Tabitha had thought she had to do it on her own; she'd made the mess, and she had to clean it up. She had been in such a hurry to get it over with that she hadn't even taken the time to ask for His guidance and His strength. Now that Tabitha was truly a child of God- His soldier, she could use His armor to help her in all life's battles and hard times.

As she sat, letting that soak in, God started spotlighting other areas in her life she needed to give to Him. All of the negative thoughts against herself were an insult to God. He was the one who had created her. She was insulting Him every time she complained about her appearance and abilities. Her negative thoughts were also destroying her and others around her. She'd let those negative thoughts come out in her actions and speech. She'd blamed others for her unhappiness, when God was the only One who could give her true happiness and joy anyway.

Lifting her eyes up to the light streaming in, Tabitha poured her honest feelings out to Him. "But God, it is so easy to look at others and compare myself to them or wish for more. It is easier to think about negatives than positives. God, I need your help. I don't know how to really let go of this. I wish you could speak out loud to me. Tell me what to do. Help me." Exhausted, Tabitha just let herself be still. She pushed everything out of her mind that was vying for attention, which was so hard. And for a moment, it was quiet.

Although God didn't speak the words out loud, He did speak to her heart. She could feel Him saying He was there to help her. He now lived in her. He gave His Word to help guide her. He gave her other Christians like her parents, Pastor, small group leaders, Christian counselors, who could help her to understand Him better. These people were older and had lived through many circumstances and learned much about God.

As if she could physically feel God's arms around her in a warm, loving hug, she knew He had answered her. She knew she had to do what she'd always fought against–talk to her family, really, completely share her feelings, and ask for help.

She was smart and knew that this battle inside her was not going to be quickly won. It was not going to happen like all those Hallmark movies and Christian romance books her mom loved to watch and read. Even though she recognized her real problem, she wasn't going to solve it in five minutes and then be all kissy face and huggy. There weren't going to be any BFF selfies with Shelby anytime soon. And no; she wasn't really stupid like she'd always tried to tell herself. Tabitha was smart enough to know that these emotions battling inside her were going to give her a constant struggle for a long time.

DIGGING DEEPER

The Battle Within: *Enlightenment*

Merriam-Webster defines *enlightenment* as "freed from ignorance and misinformation" and "based on full comprehension of the problems involved."

Tabitha felt enlightened when she realized what it meant to truly be God's child. Also, God's Word showed her the true battles she faced and would face. Lastly, she felt enlightened when she realized God was with her and would guide her through life.

1. Do you ever feel like you have no control over your emotions? Do you feel you are riding a roller coaster of feelings sometimes like Tabitha? This is normal. Even though it is normal, it is important to find a way to control the emotions.

Memorizing and reciting God's Word in difficult times, is one great way to get control of negative emotions. Colossians 3:2 is a great verse to memorize because it reminds you to keep your focus on God instead of worrying about earthly difficulties.

*Colossians 3:2: *"Set your minds on things that are above, not on things that are on earth."*

2. Paul writes in Romans 7:15, "For I do not understand my own actions. For I do not do what I want, but I do the very thing I hate." Can you relate to what he wrote? Have you ever felt like him?

*If you have felt like Paul, remember Jesus is the only One who can help us. Paul explains this in Romans 7:24-25a: *"Wretched man that I am! Who will deliver me from this body of death? Thanks be to God through Jesus Christ our Lord!"*

3. Tabitha came to realize she had never truly confessed and believed in Jesus as her Savior. Once she understood the ugliness of her sin and the great sacrifice Jesus had made for her, Tabitha prayed with complete sincerity. She then had the desire to learn more about Jesus and let Him work in her life.

Have you had a similar experience? Have you realized your need for Jesus?

If not, here are some verses to read, think and pray over. They will help explain your need for salvation and how to become a child of God:

Romans 3:10: "As it is written: *"None is righteous, no, not one;"*

Romans 3:23: *"For all have sinned and fall short of the glory of God,"*

Romans 5:12: *"Therefore, just as sin came into the world through one man, and death through sin, and so death spread to all men because all sinned—"*

Romans 6:23: *"For the wages of sin is death, but the free gift of God is eternal life in Christ Jesus our Lord."*

Romans 5:8-9: *"God shows his love for us in that while we were still sinners, Christ died for us. Since, therefore, we have now been justified by his blood, much more shall we be saved by him from the wrath of God."*

Romans 10:9-10: *" Because if you confess with your mouth that Jesus is Lord and believe in your heart that God raised him from the dead, you will be saved. For with the heart one believes and is justified, and with the mouth one confesses and is saved."*

Romans 10:13: *"For 'everyone who calls on the name of the Lord will be saved.'"*

**If the Bible verses are confusing, please find a Christian adult/friend willing to explain their importance.

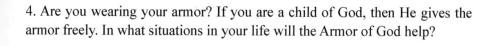

4. Are you wearing your armor? If you are a child of God, then He gives the armor freely. In what situations in your life will the Armor of God help?

Remember, you just need to put it on, pray, trust and watch God work. *"Finally, be strong in the Lord and in the strength of his might. Put on the whole armor of God, that you may be able to stand against the schemes of the devil."* Ephesians 6:10-11

5. Did you notice that Tabitha understood that all of her problems would not be solved quickly? That was a mature realization on her part. She knew that resolving the battle she was dealing with would take time. Thankfully, with God's help, she could work towards being more in control over negative emotions. Also, during the process God will begin to heal her hurt. In what ways do you think Tabitha could start working towards this goal?

*If you struggle, like Tabitha, with negative emotions and thoughts 2 Corinthians 10:3-5 (ESV) are helpful verses to memorize, *"For though we walk in the flesh, we are not waging war according to the flesh. For the weapons of our warfare are not of the flesh but have divine power to destroy strongholds. We destroy arguments and every lofty opinion raised against the knowledge of God, and take every thought captive to obey Christ,"*

YOUR NOTES

ENLIGHTENMENT

ELEVEN

HOPE

Tabitha felt a sense of freedom in finally admitting the truth: she needed help, and it was going to be a hard, continuous journey. She also felt ready to confront everything. But first, she needed to find her way out of this cave.

She literally saw hope...just like the little light streaming in from the crack in the cave ceiling. She knew there was full light if she could get out of this cave of darkness. There was complete freedom ahead; she just had to take the first steps out. She was thankful for the little stream of sunlight in the cave, but the true 'Light' was now always with her. God was her true Light. He had helped her through this whole adventure. He'd guided her through the darkness to help her really see how much she needed Him. With this new truth that wasn't just a feeling, she packed up her things and headed back into the tunnel of darkness. Tabitha would not be enveloped or controlled by the dark cave again. She would face it with bravery and strength, knowing she would travel through with God's help, His Light and Truth inside her, guiding her out.

As she took the first steps into the tunnel, she decided to start focusing on all the good in her life. With each careful high step, she named a blessing. "God, thank you for bringing me here. Thank You for helping me see my need for You. Thank you for saving me. Thank you that I am Your child. Thank You for my parents, my sister and brother. Thank You that You gave me courage to do this. Thank You for my cool shoes now protecting my feet. Thank You for my backpack. Thank You for my water bottle. Thank You for the M&M's and cashews I ate...umm even though I would love some more now...but thank You that I did have them!"

She continued until she arrived at the spot where she had taken the left. This time she took the "right" and headed out, picking back up with her thankfulness with each step, "God, thank You that I did not meet a hungry alligator or bathe in a lake of lava..." Moments, when she started to feel a little scared and questioned whether she would ever get out- when she started thinking of negatives, she would physically shake her head and tell herself to stop it. She whispered, "Do not go down that path of darkness...think of a positive...or think of a Bible verse."

The trek she was taking had some ups and downs, some slipping and sliding, even tripping and falling, but she continued until finally, she started to feel a warm breeze flow over her face. The air began to smell fresher. Light started to invade the dark. She could hear forest noises: birds chirping, leaves rustling in the wind, limbs creaking as they swayed. The sounds were music to her ears. As she continued on, the light finally defeated the darkness completely, and she was standing in rays of bright sunlight. She stood there, face lifted, and arms stretched out wide, enjoying the moment of freedom.

Then, her ears heard something even more beautiful than the forest sounds. It was her name being yelled by the people who loved her! Her parents and siblings were shouting for her, "Tabby!! Tabby!! Where are you?" Their voices sounded slightly hoarse, so they must have been shouting and looking for her this whole time. With joy and relief, she yelled back and went running in search of them. "I'm here! I'm coming! I'm here!" When they met, all together, they embraced in a warm and loving hug.

Tears of relief and joy ran down her parents' faces. After her mother got control of herself, she said, "When you didn't come to the library after about twenty minutes, we knew something had happened. We found Shelby on the soccer field and pulled her to the side to question her. She said that after you two made up..." A laugh burst out of Tabitha's mouth when she heard that, but she reigned in the laughter quickly and asked her mom to continue. Her mother looked a bit confused but continued. "Well, Shelby said after you two made up, you walked down the trail, and she went to play soccer. It appeared she wasn't going to try to help, so we started walking the trails in search of you. We have walked and shouted for you for a couple of hours, and we were just about ready to call for more help. That was when we heard the wonderful sound of your voice shouting back." Tabitha smiled with happiness and relief, knowing that God had been guiding her this whole time. If He had not helped her find her way out, her family might never have found the hidden opening into which she had journeyed.

Once all was explained and the relief and tears were abating, Tabitha's mom went into nurse mode. Feeling the bump on her head and examining the scrapes, her mom immediately decided an Urgent Care visit was needed.

After several hours in the Urgent Care, her scrapes cleaned and bandaged, Tabitha was cleared to go home with the promise that she'd return if any new pain or problems popped up. The whole family was relieved she'd come out of this experience without any major complications, and they were very ready to get back home.

Once they'd walked into their living room, Tabitha's mom wanted to hear everything that had happened. Before Tabitha could begin relaying her adventure, her brother broke in with a whine and plea for food. Everyone laughed out loud–long and hard–her sister let out a few snorts. It was the type of laughter that could bring much-needed relief after a stressful situation. They all voted to listen to Tabitha's adventure after a late dinner of their mom's famous pizza pasta.

After a yummy meal, Tabitha's brother gladly went off to play. Tabby and her sister crawled up on their parents' king size bed with them to talk. This was not only the designated area to run and do cool flips and belly flops; it was also where all their life problems seemed to be revealed and solved.

Tabitha felt so thankful to be there at that moment. She always hated to cry in front of others, but she was unable to stop the rivers flowing out of her eyes. She couldn't speak for a few minutes until the tears slowed down. This, of course, made her mother and sister cry, while her dad watched helplessly, not knowing what to do. Tabitha always loved the deer- in- the- headlights look he would give when one of them started to cry. If the tears continued for a long time, he would eventually give an awkward pat on the back. His awkwardness would evoke laughter out of them every time.

After the tears dried, Tabitha first wanted to tell them her good news. Her lips turned into a huge smile as she stated, "I got saved. I truly am God's girl now!" Tabitha explained that she had thought she had been saved in the past. However, not until she was put in a place where she came face to face with herself and her sin, did she realize the great need she'd had for God. She knew without a doubt that now she truly was a child of God.

Her parents and sister were elated! After the happy dances and squeals from her mom and sister calmed down, her parents told her they had been praying for her for a very long time. Her dad, in his serious teacher-like voice said, "Tabitha, we are so very thankful you made the decision, on your own, to truly believe and follow Jesus. The devil works in so many ways to try to confuse people and keep them away from God, even those who are surrounded by Christian influences. Many people grow up in Christian homes. They have been faithful in attending church and doing good deeds. The problem is, doing all those 'things' does not make you a child of God."

Her mom interjected, "That's right. The fact that Dad and I are Christians doesn't mean you, Sarah, and Jacob are automatically Christians. We take you to church; you memorize scripture and serve in the church, but that does not mean you are Christians. The devil wants to trick us and make us think doing good works makes us saved. But that is not true at all."

Her dad nodded his head in agreement and added, "A true believer is a person who knows she is sinful and nothing without God. Matthew 5:3, calls it being 'poor in spirit.' Without the love of God living in us, we are spiritually poor. Once we realize our sinful state, truly repent of our sins, confess that we believe Jesus died for our sins and rose again, then we are saved. But our salvation does not stop there. No! That is where just reciting a certain prayer can confuse people. If there is no true repentance, no belief and no growth, that prayer meant nothing. Once a person is truly 'saved,' she wants to start living for God."

Her dad, normally calm and quiet, was growing more excited with each sentence, "A Christian has the desire to learn more about God by reading His Word, obeying, serving Him and sharing His love with others. Doing those things does not mean you are working your way into Heaven. No way! If you are truly saved, you already have a place in Heaven. However, by doing things for God, or as the Bible says in Matthew 7:17, 'bearing good fruit,' a believer shows love and gratitude."

Taking a deep breath, like he had just finished running a race, her dad spoke again, "Tabitha, over the years my thankfulness and love for God has only grown." Jokingly, he said, "I know this may be a surprise, but...I am not perfect." After Tabitha, Sarah, and her mom laughed and rolled their eyes, her dad continued. "Daily, I make mistakes, but every time I confess those sins, God is faithful to forgive me, and He never tosses me aside. He is an amazing Father, and I want to do everything in my life to serve and praise Him. Now that you are truly His child too, I pray your love for Him will grow stronger, along with the desire to serve." After her dad finished, he pulled her into a huge hug. Then her mom and Sarah joined in.

After the hugging party ended, Tabitha's mother prodded her for information about what had happened that day. Bit by bit, the struggles came out; not just about the events surrounding Shelby, but all that Tabitha had been feeling for a very long time. Her parents, the ones who knew her the best, were shocked by all she was sharing. They had not known all the past events that had troubled her, because she had bottled them up. By refusing to share her problems and struggles, she'd allowed them to fester inside her, which kept her from healing. Each time she'd remembered the mean things Shelby had done or said, the festering wounds were picked open again. Bitterness had developed from this continuous *picking at*, and it was like an infection that never seemed to heal. Rather, it worsened.

Talking helped relieve some of the pent-up feelings Tabitha had been experiencing. Still, her parents felt she needed more help. Tabitha could not just get over this and move on. She was going to have to face the struggles, one by one, and learn ways to deal with them and those that would come in the future. Even though Tabitha was not excited and actually dreaded the idea, she agreed to start visiting a counselor at their church. She agreed to be open with her parents and share with them each evening about her day–the good and the ugly. She and her sister would start having some girls' night outings so they could become closer. Maybe they would even let their little brother join in on the fun…sometimes. Her parents felt the most important thing was that Tabitha do her best to establish a specific time to meet with God to study His word, to pray, and to listen. They said that at first it might be difficult and even seem impossible to focus, but encouraged that if she put an honest effort into seeking Him, she would start seeing Him work in her life more and more.

DIGGING DEEPER

The Battle Within: *Hope*

Merriam-Webster defines *hope* as "to cherish a desire with anticipation: to want something to happen or be true/to desire with expectation of obtainment or fulfillment."

Hope is a wonderful feeling. It gives you encouragement that your situation can change, an anticipation of better things to come. Thankfully, Tabitha not only hopes her situation will get better but finds hope in God. This hope comes from faith in God. Hebrews 11:1 states, "Faith is the assurance of things hoped for, the conviction of things not seen." Her hope in God is not a wishing hope but an assurance that God will help her through this. He is the light in her dark circumstances. Her hope in God is based on truth (God's Word) and not a feeling.

John 8:12 states, *"Again Jesus spoke to them, saying, 'I am the light of the world. Whoever follows me will not walk in darkness, but will have the light of life.'"*

1. How does this apply to Tabitha's life? How about your life? Do you feel you are walking in the darkness of sadness, anger, bitterness, self-loathing? If so, Jesus is THE light and can help you out of that darkness. All you need to do is ask Him for help, then trust and obey His Word.

Any time you feel sad, angry, or just dwell on negative thoughts, it is important to try and make a conscious effort to stop yourself. As soon as you begin feeling those negative emotions and/or thoughts, recognize them quickly. Maybe do something physical that will remind you to stop and turn from them. For example, you could shake your head "no" like Tabitha. Snap your fingers. Stomp your feet, and say, "No." Anything that can help you imagine you are turning from that "negative path" and walking down the "positive path" will work. A good Bible verse to memorize for this situation is:

*Philippians 4:8: *"Finally, brothers, whatever is true, whatever is honorable, whatever is just, whatever is pure, whatever is lovely, whatever is commendable, if there is any excellence, if there is anything worthy of praise, think about these things."*

If you can replace the negative emotions or thoughts with positives, thoughts of your blessings, you will be able to handle the tough moments and problems better.

2. Tabitha's parents brought out interesting points regarding true salvation and bearing fruit for God. Jesus taught a parable about this truth in Matthew 13:1-9 and 18-23:

"That same day Jesus went out of the house and sat beside the sea. And great crowds gathered about him, so that he got into a boat and sat down. And the whole crowd stood on the beach. And he told them many things in parables, saying: "A sower went out to sow. And as he sowed, some seeds fell along the path, and the birds came and devoured them. Other seeds fell on rocky ground, where they did not have much soil, and immediately they sprang up, since they had no depth of soil, but when the sun rose they were scorched. And since they had no root, they withered away. Other seeds fell among thorns, and the thorns grew up and choked them. Other seeds fell on good soil and produced grain, some a hundredfold, some sixty, some thirty.
He who has ears, let him hear...
Hear then the parable of the sower: When anyone hears the word of the kingdom and does not understand it, the evil one comes and snatches away what has been sown in his heart. This is what was sown along the path. As for what was sown on rocky ground, this is the one who hears the word and immediately receives it with joy, yet he has no root in himself, but endures for a while, and when tribulation or persecution arises on account of the word, immediately he falls away. As for what was sown among thorns, this is the one who hears the word, but the cares of the world and the deceitfulness of riches choke the word, and it proves unfruitful. As for what was sown on good soil, this is the one who hears the word and understands it. He indeed bears fruit and yields, in one case a hundredfold, in another sixty, and in another thirty."

The sower represents God. The seeds represent God's Word. The soil represents people. How can you apply this parable to Tabitha? Which soil could she have been before she found herself in the cave? And what soil would she be now?

3. Have you ever felt that wonderful feeling of relief when you confessed or shared something that had been heavy on your shoulders? If so, what? Describe what you felt before you shared the issue and then how you felt after.

*Tabitha's parents and family were very supportive and helpful to her. She shared her difficult issues with them. They, in turn, aided her by giving godly wisdom and seeking a Christian Counselor. If you do not have a supportive family, please do not let this stop you from finding help. First, seek God in prayer. Ask Him to guide you to a Christian adult who can assist. This could be a grandparent, aunt, uncle, teacher, pastor, etc. God loves you greatly, and He will provide people in your life who will love and support you.

YOUR NOTES

TWELVE

BLESSINGS

Two weeks later, Tabitha sat eating her favorite dessert-in-a-mug dessert and looked at the bullet journal in front of her. She was staring at a drawing she had just completed. On the left page was a sketch of a tree bent over in a sad position being choked by an ivy plant. The many vines were wrapped from the bottom of the tree all the way to the top, strangling it. On the right page was sketched the same tree, standing straighter, limbs rising to the sky, with bright green leaves and little buds. On the ground around the small tree were ivy vines lying dead, brown, and wilted. This drawing held great significance to her.

She and her mom had just finished pulling up the ivy around the tree in their backyard. Even though she was tired after the work, it was a good tired. She felt accomplished. The work had helped her to put a physical action to what she felt she was doing internally.

After the job was completed, her mother had her sit on the grass and just look at the tree and the ground around it. In her serious but loving voice she said, "Tabby, now the tree is free from what was weighing it down. Hopefully, by next spring, we will see this tree budding and full of bright green leaves waving at us. But the work doesn't stop for us today. We will have to be diligent and watchful. There is a big chance we were not able to pull up every root of that ivy plant. If we do see a vine trying to poke up from the ground, we will need to pull it up quickly. If not, before we know it, this tree will be enveloped again in a burden it was not intended to bear."

Her mother then turned her eyes and full attention on Tabitha. With watery eyes and a tender voice, she said, "Tabby, learn from this tree. You are doing so well trying to follow God, sweetheart. I see you trying daily to be obedient and grow closer to Him. But please remember to stay on guard. At times, bitter thoughts or negative emotions are going to attempt to sprout up. Recognize them as soon as you can and pluck them out quickly. Don't let yourself get buried again by all those negative thoughts and feelings. With God's help, you will grow strong in Him."

Tabitha sat thinking about that tree and her mother's advice. She felt completely amazed by God. She thought, "He is such a real and personal God. He even speaks to me through this tree in my backyard to teach me a valuable lesson. God truly does love and want the best for me."

Another activity that helped her put a physical action to what she felt internally was painting her Vans. She didn't want to look at the dingy, greyish white shoes that reminded her of the bitterness she had felt for Shelby. Tabitha only wanted to be reminded of her hope and joy in God. Every time she looked down at her Vans now, she would see the butterflies she'd painted. They would be a constant reminder of the beautiful change God worked in her.

Since the cave incident, she had visited a counselor from her church several times, and she had had many open conversations with her parents and sister. The counselor had given her homework. This homework helped her learn more about herself and gave tips on how to control her emotions. She'd also set up a nightly schedule to study her Bible.

Too, Tabitha started writing a prayer journal so she could keep her focus during prayer. She'd also begun a separate journal to record events of the day so she could document how she felt and how she'd handled them. If she'd handled them incorrectly, she'd written out a plan of action as to how to cope with them better the next time.

In her backpack, Tabitha carries a small notebook of Bible verses that she reads when she is really struggling. The counselor helped her find some Bible verses that targeted her issues. She also wrote out the most meaningful ones in her own artsy way and hung them around her bedroom.

Tabitha still struggles almost daily, but she feels she is making small improvements. She battles her emotions, sometimes expressing them wrongly; especially with her family. Thankfully though, she is now quick to realize what she is doing and usually apologizes soon after. Before, she would mull about until the next day and then begrudgingly apologize.

Tabitha has still not made any progress in finding a close friend. The thought of putting herself out there by opening up still strikes fear in her heart. Her counselor says this area will take time. She first must get comfortable with herself and the act of sharing her feelings with God and her family. A close friend will come in God's timing. He will help her through all of this, but she needs to be patient and honest with Him.

She has also begun trying to do good works and acts of charity for others. One thing Tabitha has learned about herself is that she needs to be thinking of others before herself and staying busy. When she is bored, she has too much time to think about negative things and to feel sorry for herself. She is trying to help others to keep her focus right. Tabitha happily volunteers in Children's Church. She still does not like to talk in front of others, but she has learned she can help the children in small groups with coloring, snack time, or by reading to them. They are younger and full of energy, like her brother, and they are fun to be around–most of the time.

In addition to doing her regular chores, Tabitha secretly goes around the house looking for ways to help her family when they do not expect it. She wishes she could say she doesn't complain under her breath when she is cleaning the nasty toilet, but God knows she is a work in progress.

Lastly, Tabitha has started to make lots of her paracord keychains. Instead of a superhero charm at the end, she attaches a heart charm. When she feels like God is directing, she gives them to others. If anyone asks her what the heart means, she very shyly explains John 3:16, "For God so loved the world He gave His only Son that whosoever believes in Him will not perish but have everlasting life." When she looks at the heart charm and recites the verse, she is reminded that she is loved greatly. She hopes others will know that, too, when they look at their own keychains. She's even secretly attached one to Shelby's locker.

And as for Shelby: Tabitha's parents had a conversation with the principal and Shelby's parents. Measures were put into place to make sure the bullying didn't continue, but Shelby is still Shelby. She still takes jabs at Tabitha whenever she can get away with it, but Tabitha is learning more about how to handle the situation. First, she made the very difficult decision to take a break from all social media accounts. In the beginning, it felt like torture, but after a while, she felt free. She has more time to do the crafts she loves, more time to read. She's also learned this makes her a much happier person. By not looking at the posts, she no longer plays the comparison game, and she isn't feeling as envious over what others have that she doesn't.

She's learned she cannot change Shelby, but she can pray for her. Tabitha has also realized she needs to take measures to avoid Shelby's presence. It is not cowardly to avoid people or situations that continually cause problems. Because her parents got involved, she was able to change her classes and lunch period, so she does not have to constantly be around Shelby. But when she does have to pass her in the hall or see her at an event, Tabitha tries to smile, be kind, and focus on a Bible verse.

The verse that has helped her the most has been 2 Timothy 1:7, "For God gave us a spirit not of fear but of power and love and self-control." She can't control other people. She can't control much of anything really, except how she reacts. And now, she knows her reactions need to be how God wants her to respond. Since she made the decision to believe in Jesus as her Savior, she can be honest with Him. He knows everything anyway. Without embarrassment, she can tell Him all her sinful desires and warring emotions. God will replace them with His power and love.

She now understands, God will help her control herself because:

God loves her. (John 3:16, Ephesians 2:4-5)

He created her wonderfully. (Psalm 139:14)

She is His daughter. (1 John 3:1)

His thoughts about her are precious. (Psalm 139:17)

He lives inside of her. (Romans 8:10-11, Galatians 2:20)

Because of Him she does not need to live in fear. (Psalm 27:1)

He gave her His strength and love so she can have self-control. (2 Timothy 1:7)

And most importantly, when she fails–and she will fail because she is far from perfect-He will never leave her or reject her. She is in the palm of His hand (John 10:28-29), one of His precious sheep, His daughter. He forgives and gives His mercy and grace daily. Yes, sometimes He will discipline her in a loving way to help her get back on the right path, just like caring parents do, but He does it all in love.

As Tabitha finished the last bite of her dessert, a fresh tear rolled down her cheek. It was not a tear of self-loathing or loneliness. It was a tear of amazement, joy, and thankfulness. Right now, instead of dwelling on past hurts and bathing in bitterness, she was imagining herself sitting on her Father's lap, her cheek resting on His shoulder, and His arms wrapped around her in a big hug. Tabitha knew she was dearly loved.

DIGGING DEEPER

The Battle Within: *Blessings*

Merriam-Webster defines *blessings* as "of or enjoying happiness/bringing plea-sure, contentment, or good fortune."

Tabitha feels blessed. She has come to realize the love of God is her greatest blessing. Through Him flows joy and peace. Tabitha's life will not be perfect, but by keeping her eyes on Him, she will be able to see her blessings–big and small.

1. Tabitha's story is not a "wrap it up, and tie it with a pretty bow" happy end-ing. Though her life will be filled with the joy only God can give and many, many happy moments, she will also be in a life-long battle over many issues. She will make mistakes and have hardships, but the end of the story, the end of her life, will result in a perfectly happy forever. She will come face to face with God in heaven. She will hear, "Well done, good and faithful servant. You have been faithful over a little; I will set you over much. Enter into the joy of your master" (Matthew 25:21, ESV). She won't hear this because she lived a perfect life, but because she trusted God's Son, Jesus, as her Savior and chose to live a life for Him.

God wants to say those words to you also! Choose to focus on all the blessings God has given you. Bask in His love and joy. Then, live each day to the fullest. Share His love and joy with all those around you, even the difficult people in your life!

Memorize the Bible verses below to keep your focus in the right place:

*Philippians 4:4-8: *"Rejoice in the Lord always; again, I will say, rejoice. Let your reasonableness be known to everyone. The Lord is at hand; do not be anxious about anything, but in everything by prayer and supplication with thanksgiving let your requests be made known to God. And the peace of God, which surpasses all understanding, will guard your hearts and your minds in Christ Jesus."*

*Psalm 67:1-2: *"May God be gracious to us and bless us, and make His face to shine upon us, that Your way may be known on earth, your saving power among all the nations."*

2. Are you disappointed that there was not a resolution in the relationship between Tabitha and Shelby? What would you have liked to have seen happen between them?

The truth is, there will be many people in your life who may never like you or apologize for a wrong they have done. You cannot control how other people behave, but you can control how you respond.

3. After reading the plan Tabitha has set up for herself, are there any steps that you could take yourself? If so, start them immediately. Don't let the busyness of life prevent you from starting your journey to get closer to God. He is waiting with arms wide open for you.

**If you feel like Tabitha did at the beginning of her story please ask for help from your family, Pastor, teachers, friends, and/or Christian Counselors. Talking through a problem and seeking help is very important.

BLESSINGS

Below are more resources that can help you through difficult situations in your life; especially situations that find you battling your emotions:

*Memorize Bible verses. God's Word can focus your mind on Him and what He would like you to do. It can show you how to act in a Christ-like manner.

*Pray! Tell God everything. He wants to hear from you. But please make sure you spend time listening for Him to speak to your heart. If you have a specific prayer request for yourself or others, a good way to remember to pray throughout the whole day is to set a timer on your phone. When the alarm chimes, you will remember to pray for the specific matter.

*Get involved in church. Join a youth group, Bible study group, or Bible Club. Being with fellow brothers and sisters in Christ can give you encouragement and support.

*Think of others before yourself. Look for ways to help others.

*Take a break, or even give up social media.

*Set time limits for being on your cell phone.

*Guard your heart and mind regarding what you listen to and watch.

*Eat healthily.

*Exercise regularly.

*Get plenty of sleep every night.

* A good way to remind yourself that you are wonderfully created by God is (with your parent's permission) to write Psalm 139:14, with a sharpie, paint, or a dry erase marker, around the outside edges of your bedroom mirror.

YOUR NOTES

BLESSINGS

ACTIVITIES

Letter From Jesus

Jesus' prayer for you from John 17:

When Jesus had spoken these words, he lifted up his eyes to heaven, and said, "Father, the hour has come; glorify your Son that the Son may glorify you, since you have given him authority over all flesh, to give eternal life to all whom you have given him. And this is eternal life, that they know you, the only true God, and Jesus Christ whom you have sent. I glorified you on earth, having accomplished the work that you gave me to do. And now, Father, glorify me in your own presence with the glory that I had with you before the world existed. I have manifested your name to the people whom you gave me out of the world. Yours they were, and you gave them to me, and they have kept your word. Now they know that everything that you have given me is from you. For I have given them the words that you gave me, and they have received them and have come to know in truth that I came from you; and they have believed that you sent me. I am praying for them. I am not praying for the world but for those whom you have given me, for they are yours. All mine are yours, and yours are mine, and I am glorified in them. And I am no longer in the world, but they are in the world, and I am coming to you. Holy Father, keep them in your name, which you have given me, that they may be one, even as we are one. While I was with them, I kept them in your name, which you have given me. I have guarded them, and not one of them has been lost except the son of destruction, that the Scripture might be fulfilled. But now I am coming to you, and these things I speak in the world, that they may have my joy fulfilled in themselves. I have given them your word, and the world has hated them because they are not of the world, just as I am not of the world. I do not ask that you take them out of the world, but that you keep them from the evil one. They are not of the world, just as I am not of the world. Sanctify them in the truth; your word is truth. As you sent me into the world, so I have sent them into the world. And for their sake I consecrate myself, that they also may be sanctified in truth. I do not ask for these only, but also for those who will believe in me through their word, that they may all be one, just as you, Father, are in me, and I in you, that they also may be in us, so that the world may believe that you have sent me. The glory that you have given me I have given to them, that they may be one even as we are one, I in them and you in me, that they may become perfectly one, so that the world may know that you sent me and loved them even as you loved me. Father, I desire that they also, whom you have given me, may be with me where I am, to see my glory that you have given me because you loved me before the foundation of the world. O righteous Father, even though the world does not know you, I know you, and these know that you have sent me. I made known to them your name, and I will continue to make it known, that the love with which you have loved me may be in them, and I in them."

Love,
Jesus

Label Tabitha's Armor Of God

The Armor of God
Ephesians 6:10-18

The Word of God

Tabitha's Homemade Scratch Off Card

Directions:
1. Get a sheet of paper (printer paper, construction paper, index card, etc.).
2. Draw a picture, write a Bible verse, a note, etc..
3. Break off a piece of wax from a candle, and rub it over your picture.
4. Paint over the wax with a dark color of paint.
5. Let it dry.
6. Then give this encouraging picture/note to a family member or friend to scratch off! Once they scratch off the paint and wax, they will be encouraged by the note!

**Here are a few examples...

"For God so loved the world, that he gave his only Son,

that whoever believes in him

should not perish but have eternal life."

John 3:16

"Again, Jesus spoke to them, saying, 'I am the light of the world.

Whoever follows me will not walk in darkness,
but will have the light of life.'" John 8:12

"This is the day that the LORD has made;
let us rejoice and be glad in it." Psalm 118:24

My Bucket List

NOW SOON FUTURE

_____ _____ _____

_____ _____ _____

_____ _____ _____

_____ _____ _____

_____ _____ _____

_____ _____ _____

_____ _____ _____

_____ _____ _____

Tabitha's Mug Recipes

Apple Crisp in a Mug

Ingredients:
1 apple
1 tbsp all-purpose flour
2 ½ tbsp brown sugar
Pinch of salt
1 ½ tbsp coconut oil
2 tbsp quick oats
Dash of cinnamon

Directions:
Cut apple up in thin and small pieces. Mix the apple pieces and all other ingredients in a bowl. Pour into a mug. Microwave for 45 seconds to 1 minute. If not completely done, cook 20 more seconds. Enjoy!

Chocolate Strawberry Cake in a Mug

Ingredients:
¼ cup all-purpose flour
¼ tsp baking powder
Dash of salt
2 tbsp sugar
½ tsp vanilla extract
2 tbsp butter
3 tbsp milk
1 large strawberry (cut up in small pieces)
1 tbsp chocolate chips

Directions:
Mix together all dry ingredients in a mug. Next, add in the wet ingredients with strawberry and chocolate chips. Microwave cake mixture for 2 ½ to 3 minutes. Enjoy!

Tabitha's Paracord Keychain

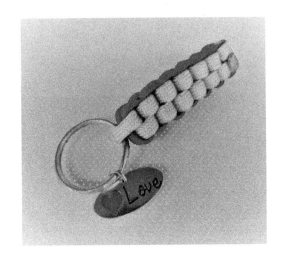

Supplies:
2 – 24 inches of paracord
Key ring
Charm
Scissors
Matches

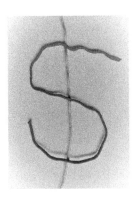

Make an "S" shape over the other vertical paracord.

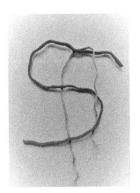

Move the vertical paracord over the top part of the "S" and under the bottom part of the "S."

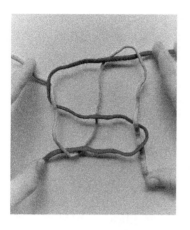 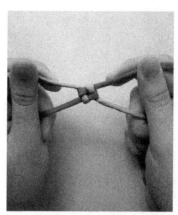

Pull each of the four ends evenly at the same time to form the box shape.

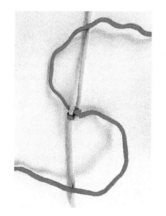 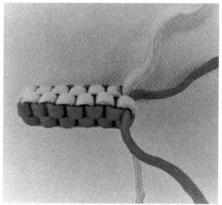

Repeat the same steps to make your paracord keychain
the length you would like.

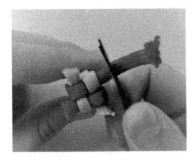

Cut the remaining paracord ¼ inch from the base.

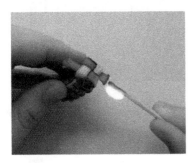

Burn the edges.

Smash the melted ends with the edge of your scissors.

Attach the key ring and charm to the loop at the other end of the paracord.

Bible Verse Note Cards

Create a nice border for your note cards to write down your favorite bible veres.

Below are a few examples...

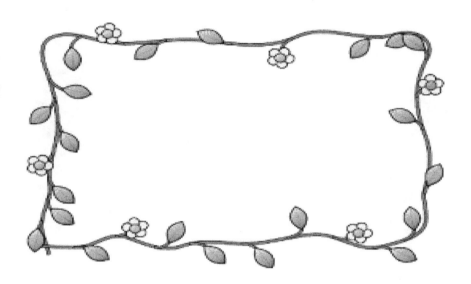

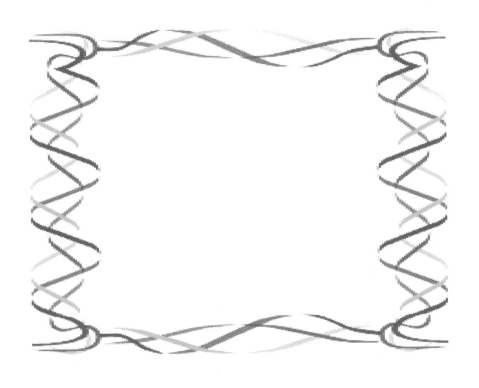

CITATIONS

"Dictionary by Merriam-Webster: America's Most-trusted Online Dictionary."
Merriam-Webster. Accessed July 1, 2020. http://www.merriam-webster.com/.

"Print and Color Mandalas Online." Print and Color Mandalas Online. Accessed January 10, 2021. http://colormandala.com/.

ABOUT THE AUTHOR

Wendy Perry is a wife, mother of four and missionary to the Deaf. She grew up in North Carolina, and graduated from Gardner Webb University, with a degree in American Sign Language. For the past seven years, she and her family have lived in Nicaragua. Her oldest son returned to the United States and is now married and working in their home church. Her oldest daughter is also in the States pursuing her college degree.

In addition to her roles as wife, mother, homeschool teacher for her two teenagers and her work with the Deaf Ministry, Wendy is learning how to speak Spanish with her southern drawl and how to communicate in Nicaraguan Sign Language. Her greatest passion is to live for God, wherever He leads, and to share His love and truth with all those she encounters.

CPSIA information can be obtained
at www.ICGtesting.com
Printed in the USA
LVHW082009100221
678988LV00013B/825

9 781952 840043